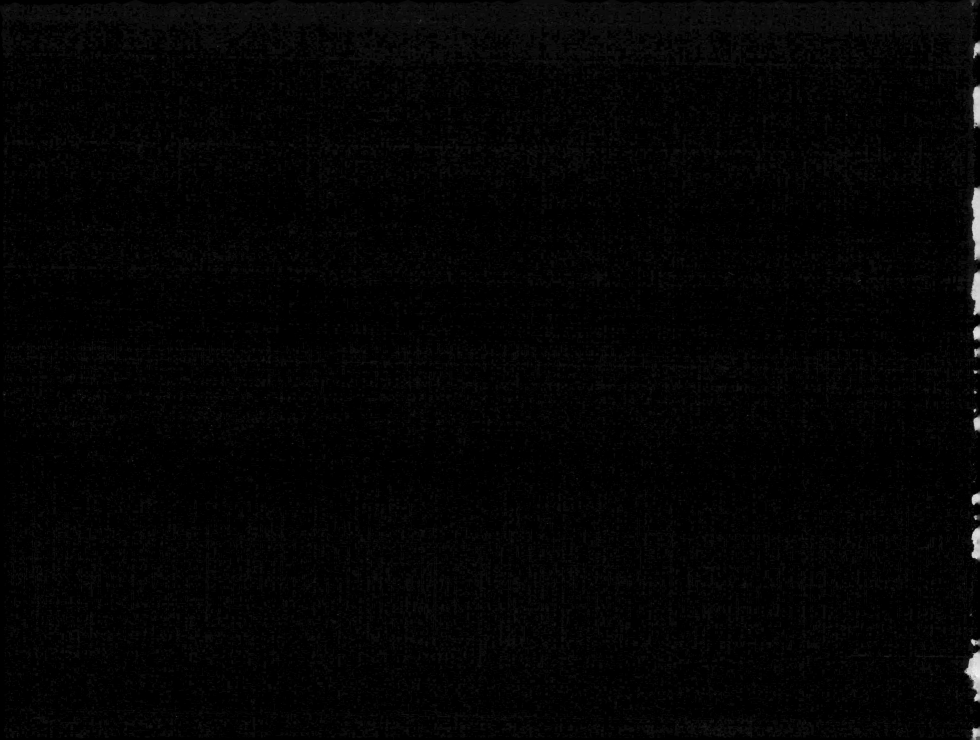

King's College London

Contributions to biomedicine *a continuing story*

Edited by
Claire Taylor &
Gwyn Williams

The original coat of arms used by the College, with supporters and motto
unique to King's College London. The motto reads:

'Sancte et Sapienter'
'With Holiness and Wisdom'

First published 2006

Published by:
King's College London School of Medicine
Hodgkin Building
Guy's Campus
London
SE1 1UL

ISBN 0-9552620-0-3
ISBN 978-0-9552620-0-5

Designed by Helen Senior Associates & Matt Sarraf
Printed by Cambridge University Press

Contents

Foreword

We are delighted to introduce this book which celebrates the achievements of our colleagues past and present. Their work has, and continues to shape the world of biomedicine in which we operate today. King's College London is immensely proud of its heritage in this field, the foundations of which go back centuries to the origins of St Thomas' Hospital in the twelfth century, Bethlem, Guy's, King's College and Maudsley Hospitals – all great institutions of healing in their own right. It has been further enriched by the mergers with King's in the 1980s and 1990s of Chelsea College, Queen Elizabeth College, the Institute of Psychiatry and the United Medical and Dental Schools of Guy's and St Thomas' Hospitals.

To be truly pioneering requires tenacity and a spirit of enquiry. This book highlights just some of the remarkable contributions made by the most influential people who have created our cumulative history. They span three centuries – from the seventeenth century anatomists whose work led to a more specific understanding of the human body; to Thomas Hodgkin, Richard Bright and Thomas Addison who in the nineteenth century were at the forefront of the birth of medical science in Britain; and to Rosalind Franklin's and Maurice Wilkins's work on the understanding of the structure of DNA in the twentieth century.

Robert Lechler   Rick Trainor

King's critical mass of scientists and clinical academics continue their rich legacy and through our partnerships with the Guy's, King's College and St Thomas' Hospitals and the South London and Maudsley Mental Health Trust, sustain research centred on patients and their relief from illness.

The College and its constituent institutions have also been a training ground for those who have employed their knowledge and skills worldwide and reflect dedication to the advancement of knowledge, learning and understanding in the service of society.

Professor Robert Lechler
Vice-Principal (Health)
King's College London

Professor Rick Trainor
Principal
King's College London

While a full list of acknowledgments is detailed on page 113,
we would specifically like to thank a number of individuals for
their enthusiasm and support during the production of this book
and for their particular contributions in its making.

We thank Christine Kenyon Jones, for her ideas, advice,
experience and support as well as her authorship;
Áine Mannion for research and for sourcing literally hundreds
of photographs and images;
Eleanor Margolies for research and comments on drafts
throughout the book's production;
Christine Ayre for her readiness to give
instant help and advice;
Peter Graham for his help and patience;
finally Helen Senior for art directing and
with whom it has been a pleasure to work.

1107

The Augustinian priory of St Mary Overie establishes an infirmary for pilgrims just south of London Bridge. In 1173 the infirmary takes the name of St Thomas after Thomas Beckett's canonisation that year.

1212

St Thomas' Hospital is destroyed by fire and rebuilt.

1247

Bethlem Hospital is founded in Bishopsgate, as a priory dedicated to St Mary of Bethlehem.

1403

Bethlem's records first show it is being used to care for people with mental illness.

1540

St Thomas' Hospital is closed during the Reformation. It is reinstated in 1553 by King Edward VI.

1561

First record of medical instruction at St Thomas'.

1656

Thomas Wharton writes *Adenographia*, the first known contribution to the scientific understanding of the body from this institution.

King's College London: a brief history

King's College London is a major international research-led teaching institution. With six health schools and a close alignment with its partner National Health Service Trusts (Guy's and St Thomas' NHS Foundation Trust, King's College Hospital Trust and the South London and Maudsley Trust), King's is at the forefront of biomedical research. In 2005 the College was awarded its fourth MRC Centre, a quarter of the total number of MRC Centres in the UK.

The Schools of Medicine, Biomedical & Health Sciences and the Dental Institute are located at the world-famous Guy's, King's College and St Thomas' Hospitals. The Institute of Psychiatry is at the equally famous Maudsley Hospital, and the Florence Nightingale School of Nursing is located at the Waterloo Campus, near to its original foundation at St Thomas' Hospital.

King's College London was founded in 1829 as a university college in the tradition of the Church of England. When the University of London was established in 1836, King's became one of its founding colleges.

King's included a Medical Department from the beginning in 1829. However, as a result of many mergers, including those with the United Medical and Dental Schools of Guy's and St Thomas' Hospitals

1724
The building of Guy's Hospital begins with funds given by Thomas Guy. The hospital was intended for 400 sick persons 'who might not be received into other hospitals from being deemed incurable' and for the care of up to 20 'lunatics'. The first patients are admitted to the hospital in 1726.

1768
Guy's and St Thomas' Hospitals formalise their joint arrangements for teaching medical students as the 'United Hospitals of the Borough'.

1815
Poet John Keats undertakes training at Guy's as an apothecary.

1825
Arrangements for teaching medical students at Guy's and St Thomas' Hospitals are separated.

1828
James Blundell reports in *The Lancet* his studies on the first human to human blood transfusions.

1829
The Duke of Wellington (above right) fights a duel with the Earl of Winchilsea in defence of his simultaneous role in the foundation of King's College and his support of the Roman Catholic Relief Act. King George signs the royal charter of King's College London.

1831
Opening of King's College London.

and the Institute of Psychiatry, King's has a cumulative history of contributions to biomedicine over several centuries.

Travellers and incurables
St Thomas' Hospital has its origins in a small infirmary attached to the Augustinian Priory of St Mary Overie (now Southwark Cathedral) just south of London Bridge. The Priory, founded in 1107, looked after sick and needy travellers using the only bridge over the Thames. The appointment in 1703 of Dr Richard Mead, the most eminent physician of the day, added considerably to the prestige of the hospital. Mead was a great friend of Thomas Guy, a wealthy bookseller and a governor of St Thomas'. In 1721, Guy built a hospital for the 'incurables' discharged from St Thomas' with nowhere else to go. His will stated that 'Guy's Hospital' should thereafter be open to all and have its own governing body. In the early years, medical training took place at St Thomas' through a system of apprenticeships (documented in records dated 1561), and it was put on a formal footing in the late seventeenth century. The educational links between St Thomas' and Guy's remained close even after the hospitals became separate institutions. In the eighteenth century, lectures and operations were attended by the students

1836
Robert Bentley Todd is appointed to King's and radically reforms medical education.

1839
Foundation of the University of London. Degrees of the University of London are first awarded to King's students in 1839.

King's College Hospital is established in Portugal Street, north of the Strand

1860
Florence Nightingale establishes the School of Nursing at St Thomas' Hospital.

1871
St Thomas' Hospital moves to its present site in Lambeth to make way for the building of London Bridge railway station.

1888
Guy's is the first general hospital in the country to establish a dental school.

1895
South-Western Polytechnic (later Chelsea College which merges with King's in 1985) opens.

of both hospitals, and in 1768 this arrangement was formalised. However, when in 1825 St Thomas' Hospital decided to enforce the lapsed system of showing tickets for the operating theatre, a riot broke out. The police were called and six medical students arrested. This riot, and arguments over the ownership of museum specimens and Astley Cooper's successor, led to the formal breaking of links between St Thomas' and Guy's, and the establishment of a

separate medical school at Guy's. The extension of the railway from London Bridge to Charing Cross forced St Thomas' Hospital to move: temporarily in the Surrey Gardens music hall – where the giraffe house was used as a cholera ward and the elephant house as a dissecting room – and then in 1871 into a new hospital building opposite the Houses of Parliament. Florence Nightingale established her school of nursing at St Thomas' in 1860.

Bethlem
Bethlem Royal Hospital was founded in 1247 by Simon Fitzmary as a priory dedicated to St Mary of Bethlehem. The first definite evidence of its use to house mentally ill patients dates from 1403, making it probably the oldest mental hospital in the world. In 1676 Bethlem moved to Moorfields. In 1815 it moved to St George's Fields, Southwark. Some of its former buildings there now form part of the Imperial

1913
The new King's College Hospital opens at Denmark Hill.

1918
To meet shortages of doctors caused by the War, King's becomes the first mixed medical school in London. Guy's follows suit in 1947 and St Thomas' in 1949.

1923
The Maudsley Hospital opens as a London County Hospital for the early treatment of acute mental illness.

1948
On the creation of the NHS, the medical schools of Guy's, King's College and St Thomas' Hospitals become independent of the hospitals.
The Maudsley's medical school is renamed the Institute of Psychiatry.

1949
Harold Ridley performs the world's first ever intraocular lens implantation at St Thomas'.

1953
Maurice Wilkins and Rosalind Franklin publish in *Nature* their structural studies of DNA.

1962
Maurice Wilkins is awarded the Nobel Prize for Physiology or Medicine for his part, with Rosalind Franklin, in the discovery of the structure of DNA.

War Museum. In 1930 the Hospital relocated again to Beckenham, South London.

In 1948, Bethlem was united with the Maudsley Hospital and in that same year the Maudsley's medical school became the independent Institute of Psychiatry in the University of London.

The medical school as part of a university
When the Medical Department of King's began, there were no formal courses, the timetable was chaotic, and students found it difficult to obtain clinical instruction and hospital experience. Robert Bentley Todd joined King's as Professor of Physiology and Morbid Anatomy in 1836. He radically reformed medical education and campaigned persuasively for the establishment of a new teaching hospital. King's College Hospital was officially opened in 1840, housed in a former workhouse near the King's site on the Strand. In 1913, King's College Hospital moved to Denmark Hill. A dental school and dental hospital were established there in 1923. King's differed from the older teaching hospitals in that the medical staff had scientific colleagues from other academic faculties. To this can perhaps be attributed the hospital's encouragement and support of innovative figures such as Joseph Lister.

HRH Princess Royal opens the Weston Education Centre, King's Denmark Hill Campus, 1997.

Archbishop Desmond Tutu opens the £7 million infection and immunity laboratories in 2004.

Wellcome Trust Director, Mark Walport (centre) opens £11 million genetics laboratories in 2005.

HRH Princess Royal with Lord and Lady Wolfson at the opening of The Wolfson Centre for Age Related Diseases in 2005.

1983

King's College School of Medicine and Dentistry reunites with King's. The United Medical and Dental Schools of Guy's and St Thomas' Hospitals (UMDS) are formed.

1988

Sir James Black wins Nobel Prize for Physiology or Medicine for the development of beta blockers and anti-ulcer drugs.

1997

The Institute of Psychiatry joins King's.

1998

UMDS merges with King's.

2001

The Chancery Lane Library, converted from the former Public Record Office building, opens. After a two year, £35 million transformation, it is renamed the Maughan Library in 2002.
The library holds the historical medical collection of the Foyle Special Collections library.

2003-2006

King's completes a wide range of redevelopment projects to enhance facilities for biomedical research, including:

a £30 million investment at the Guy's Campus for state-of-the-art laboratories for infection and immunity research and genetics research and The Wolfson Centre for Age Related Diseases – the UK's first research centre in this area;

a £16 million building at the Institute of Psychiatry for The Medical Research Council Social, Genetic and Developmental Psychiatry Centre for research into genetic and environmental factors affecting mental health;

the Centre for Cell and Integrative Biology at the Denmark Hill Campus. The £25 million building is completed in 2006 for stem cell research into cardiovascular disease, organ transplantation and neurodegenerative diseases.

In 1983 the King's College Hospital School of Medicine rejoined King's College London (from which it had separated in 1908). The Institute of Psychiatry joined King's in 1997, and in 1998 the United Medical and Dental Schools of Guy's and St Thomas' Hospitals (UMDS) and King's College formally merged creating one of the largest centres for medical training and biomedical research in the UK.

William Cheselden giving an anatomical demonstration to six spectators in the anatomy theatre of the Barber-Surgeons' Company. By Charles Phillips, circa 1730.

Thomas Wharton
(1614-1673)

William Cheselden FRS
(1688-1752)

Sir Astley Paston Cooper
FRS (1768-1841)

Sir William Bowman FRS
(1816-1892)

Lionel Beale FRS
(1828-1906)

Anatomy acts

Qualities required of a surgeon:
'He must know his anatomy; for all authors write against surgeons
that work in man's body not knowing the anatomy'   Thomas Vicary (c1490-1573)

Thomas Vicary's telling statement took note of the
impact of the new approach to anatomy stemming
from the work of Vesalius in Padua in 1543. He based
his dissections and conclusions on observed fact and
enquiry, replacing the centuries-old regurgitation of
ancient anatomical texts which had prevented original
thought. In Britain the anatomists, who doubled as
physicians and surgeons, continued the new science of
careful dissection, description and deduction of
function of the human body's structures.

It was against this background that the earliest
contributions to the understanding of human anatomy
at this institution were made by Thomas Wharton
(1614-1673) in the seventeenth century, just 100 years
after two landmarks in the study of anatomy in
England. Only in the sixteenth century had human
cadaveric dissection become regularly practised in
England by the designated officers of the Barbers and
Surgeons. Furthermore it was not until the 1570s that
anatomical texts became available in English.

Thomas Wharton

A physician at St Thomas' from 1657, Wharton's main
work was to understand the anatomy of the glands and
to set this against the simultaneous discoveries of the
lymphatic and nervous systems. In 1656 he published
his Latin treatise *Adenographia*, a description of the
glands of the entire body, which he dedicated to the
Royal College of Physicians. *Adenographia*, which
Wharton published at his own expense, was the first
thorough account of the glands of the human body.
Then, the nerves and lymphatics were thought to be
vascular in nature and were not considered important
in understanding the functions of the human body.
Wharton stated that glands excreted fluid from lymph,
conveying it to nerves, and also evacuated waste
material from the nervous system into lymphatic
channels. He described the ovaries, the testes and
their production of sperm, the breasts and their
production of milk and showed why the tongue,
spleen and brain were not glands. All this was the fruit

of careful dissection of human and animal bodies. At that time, this work was at the forefront of anatomy. In addition to describing the duct of the submandibular salivary gland (Wharton's duct) and the jelly of the umbilical cord (Wharton's jelly), Wharton also named the thyroid gland.

Wharton was at St Thomas' Hospital for the majority of his career. He was one of the few physicians not to flee London during the plague of 1665 and remained at the hospital to treat patients. His commitment to duty was commended and noted by the Royal College of Physicians. Wharton was described as one of 'miners of nature' for his work on describing the glands. He paved the way towards a physiological understanding of human anatomical structures and fluids.

William Cheselden

William Cheselden (1688-1752) was one of the most eminent surgeons and anatomists of the eighteenth century and was instrumental in establishing surgery as a profession separately from barbers.

Following his medical training at St Thomas' and without a hospital appointment, Cheselden began private tuition. At that time there was little formal medical training in Britain. In 1711, at the age of 22, Cheselden instigated a course of 35 lectures on anatomy, comparative anatomy and animal economy (physiology). These are considered to be some of the first pre-clinical training in Britain. His published works further established his position as a key figure in the teaching of anatomy. His first major work, *The Anatomy of the Human Body*, was published in 1713 and was to become a standard anatomical text for well over the next one hundred years, achieving 13 editions. Its popularity was in part due to the fact that it was written in English rather than Latin.

Cover of William Cheselden's The Anatomy of the Human Body. Published in 1713 it became a standard anatomical text for well over the next one hundred years.

Front page of Cheselden's Osteographia published in 1733 and which Cheselden illustrated himself.

Osteographia or the *Anatomy of Bones*, published in 1733, was to become Cheselden's most important anatomical work. It was the first full and accurate description of human osseous anatomy. The bones were shown life size and illustrated by Cheselden himself.

Appointed assistant surgeon at St Thomas' Hospital in 1718, Cheselden was made a principal surgeon within a year, enabling him to develop his own operative techniques, especially for bladder stone extraction. Cheselden developed the 'high' operation to remove stones through a suprapubic incision, published in *A Treatise on the High Operation for the Stone* (1723). The operation enabled a much faster procedure and drastically reduced operative mortality to less than 10 per cent.

Cheselden was instrumental in the negotiations to separate surgery from the Company of Barber-Surgeons. In July 1745 the Company of Surgeons (now the Royal College of Surgeons) was established with John Ranby

as master and Cheselden as senior warden. Cheselden was elected master in 1746.

Sir Astley Paston Cooper

Astley Paston Cooper (1768-1841) was an accomplished and skilful surgeon at Guy's and St Thomas' Hospitals. He was the first to operate on the major blood vessels and became most well known for his work on inguinal hernias, however he was not a surgeon to forget the scientific side of his profession. He was also an original anatomist and highly regarded teacher of the subject.

'Nothing is known in our profession by guess; observation on the diseased living, examination of the dead, and experiments upon living animals, are the only sources of true knowledge' wrote Cooper. As a pupil of Henry Cline at St Thomas' and John Hunter, Cooper acquired an aptitude for dissection and experimentation which never left him. He was an advocate of comparative anatomy and his animal experiments included the dissection of an elephant. He was lecturer on anatomy at the Royal College of Surgeons, which he presided over twice in his career. A teacher of both anatomy and surgery, he stressed practical demonstrations over didactism and gained the respect and admiration of his students, who packed the lecture theatres. One of his pupils included poet John Keats (see pages 109-110) who trained for a year at Guy's in 1815-1816.

Cooper's chief anatomy publications were works on testes, breast and the inguinal region. *The Anatomy and Surgical Treatment of Inguinal and Congenital Hernias* was regarded by many at the time as a seminal work in the field. In it he first describes the anatomy of the cremasteric fascia, the pectineal ligament and the transversalis fascia. Cooper's *Anatomy of the Breast* in 1840 was the first detailed analysis of the anatomy and physiology of the breast.

Among his best works is his description of the thymus; he described the 'reservoir' of the thymus as lined by smooth mucous membrane and running spirally, not straight, through the gland. Cooper also described several new anatomical structures including Cooper's ligaments, the suspensory ligaments of the breast, and Cooper's pubic ligament.

Illustration from Cooper's Anatomy of the Breast 1840.

Sir William Bowman

William Bowman (1816-1892) became known in his career as a leading ophthalmologist. However he had already made his reputation with his early anatomical work at King's College London and King's College Hospital. Bowman capitalised on the use of microscopes, which had just begun to take anatomy into new areas of understanding and conjecture, and his work had a profound influence on anatomy by relating microscopic structure to function.

With Robert Bentley Todd at King's and King's College Hospital he published *The Physiological Anatomy and Physiology of Man* (1845-56), a pioneering work in physiology and histology. Bowman studied organ tissues, the structure and function of voluntary

muscle, the kidneys, the eye (see page 104) and the liver. His name is perpetuated in several structures. Best known is Bowman's capsule, which he described surrounding each glomerulus in the kidney and continuous with the renal tubules. This was of prime importance to his filtration theory of urine formation. Bowman presented these findings in 1842 in his paper *On the Structure and Use of Malpighian Bodies of the Kidney* to the Royal Society and he was awarded the Royal Medal. Also named after him are Bowman's glands in the olfactory mucosa and Bowman's membrane in the cornea.

Lionel Beale

Lionel Beale (1828-1906) was Professor of Physiology and subsequently Medicine at King's. His interests were microscopy and chemical pathology and he was a prominent advocate for the application of these new techniques to clinical medicine.

He worked with Bowman on the histology of renal structures and muscle fibres. He further developed the clinical and practical aspects of microscopy, pioneering the practice of fixing of tissues by injections to prevent alterations after death and the use of oil-immersion magnification. In 1854 he published the influential *The Microscope and its Application to Clinical Medicine*, setting out the procedures for microscopic examination of blood, urine, tumours and parasites.

The Gordon Anatomical Museum

King's Gordon Museum is the largest medical museum in the UK and contains some rare and unique artefacts including Lister's antiseptic spray and the original specimens of kidneys, adrenal glands and lymph nodes which led Bright, Addison and Hodgkin to describe the conditions that bear their names (see

Joseph Towne

John Hilton

Towne's wax model collection

Astley Cooper secured the appointment of Joseph Towne as wax modeller to Guy's Hospital Medical School, a post he held for 53 years. In that time he produced 200 anatomical models, based on the dissections of demonstrator John Hilton. Towne's models are on display today in the Gordon Medical Museum at the Guy's Hospital Campus and are still used for teaching. Towne was awarded many prizes for his works including the silver medal from the Royal Society for Arts.

Joseph Towne's models are on display today in the Gordon Museum.

Robert Gordon, Governor of Guy's Hospital (from 1898) and Gordon Museum benefactor.

pages 17-20). The Sir Astley Cooper collection is also on display in the Museum, containing examples of his surgical innovations as well as the pre-operative paintings of Lam Qua and the Joseph Towne anatomical, dermatological and pathology wax model collection, still used today in medical teaching.

There has been a collection of specimens and other medical ephemera on the Guy's Campus since 1802, and this formed the basis of the Medical School's first museum which opened in 1826 and whose curator was Thomas Hodgkin. The Gordon Museum was opened at Guy's in 1905 as a result of a donation by Robert Gordon, then Governor of Guy's Hospital, of £45,000 to support pathology research and teaching.

The Museum's primary function has always been to help train medical professionals to diagnose disease and this is in part achieved by using the UK's largest collection of pathology specimens. There are some 8,000 pots which have been assimilated over 400 years, showing classic and rare cases of disease.

2005 marked the centenary year of the Gordon Museum. The collection continues to grow. It is one of the few medical museums in the country that continues to accept new specimens to document new and emerging diseases like HIV/AIDS. Current projects include analysing DNA extracted from organs to discover whether the patient has suffered from malaria, and scanning larger specimens using magnetic resonance imaging (MRI) to gain insights into the diseases' effects on the organs' internal structure.

The Museum is also a place of private study particularly using computer-aided learning facilities, and continues to be a unique and inspiring environment for students and staff at King's.

The Gordon Museum.

35th edition of *Gray's Anatomy*.

Gray's Anatomy *at King's*

Gray's Anatomy is recognised the world over as the ultimate anatomical text. Leading King's anatomists have been responsible for 76 years of editorship in Gray's 147 year history. It was first published in 1858 and is now in its 39th edition.

It was first edited at this institution by T B Johnson in 1930 and is presently edited by Professor Susan Standring at King's who first appeared on the editorial board in 1973. The current edition has undergone the most radical revision since the first 1858 edition. It is now organised by body region instead of body system,

describing anatomy regionally and in the way practising clinicians use their anatomical knowledge. *Gray's Anatomy 39e* is the first time the text has been offered as an 'E-dition'. *Gray's* today still retains its reputation as the 'doctor's bible'.

Professor Standring will remain Editor-in-Chief of the 40th edition which will be published in 2008, marking 150 years of continuous publication.

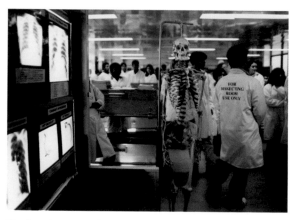

'The dissecting room at King's' photographed by Karen Ingham, and featured in her book *Anatomy Lessons* published by Dewi Lewis. Traditional cadaveric dissection, practised for centuries in the medical school is still an integral part of medical training at King's today.

Richard Bright FRS
(1789-1858)

Thomas Addison
(1795-1860)

Thomas Hodgkin
(1798-1866)

Birth of medical science in Britain: Guy's 'Three Greats'

One of the greatest leaps forward in the history of medicine was made in the nineteenth century when scientific method was applied to the study of illness, coupling together the study of living patients and the findings of postmortem examinations.

Thomas Addison, Richard Bright and Thomas Hodgkin, sometimes called 'the three great men of Guy's', worked simultaneously at Guy's Hospital. Their historical reputation is not just for their eponymous diseases but also for being three of the first to adopt scientific methodology in the study of diseases.

The appliance of science

Until the sixteenth century, knowledge of the human body was drawn from ancient texts by writers such as Hippocrates and Galen. In contrast, the anatomical studies of Vesalius (1514-1564), based on detailed observation of human dissections, showed an inquiring approach to new knowledge. In the following century, the discovery of the circulation of the blood by William Harvey, and the work of Thomas Willis and Richard Lower on the circulations of the brain and lungs, showed the benefits of this new approach. However, the improved understanding of anatomy had little immediate effect on the understanding of disease, let alone medical practice.

It was not until the nineteenth century that science exploded, with medical developments concentrated in France. Marie-François-Xavier Bichat and René Theophile Hyacinthe Laënnec led the way in developing methods of observing physical signs, such as Laënnec's invention of the stethoscope. Paris became a mecca for studying medicine. Those returning from Paris spread new ideas in their native cities, with Vienna and London particularly benefitting. In the 1830s, the first two medical schools in London were founded at University College and King's College London. Meanwhile new medical societies and journals and the availability for study of large numbers of patients in the new hospitals provided fertile ground for the development of medical science. It is against this background that Addison, Bright and Hodgkin made their contributions.

As practising physicians, they observed and recorded symptoms and signs of illness in their patients and related these signs to postmortem findings. They spent many hours each day in the postmortem room – a practice unheard of then. They built up clusters of cases, relating clinical features to pathological anatomy in order to categorize and make sense of prevalent diseases. This was a revolutionary approach at the time, and attracted criticism and disapproval. But eventually their methods were recognized in Britain and abroad as the most powerful tool available to medicine.

Thomas Hodgkin was the first curator of the anatomy museum at Guy's (now the Gordon Museum). He catalogued the museum's specimens to demonstrate the effects of disease on the body's organs and tissues.

Thomas Hodgkin

Thomas Hodgkin (1798-1866) was born into a Quaker family and his strict upbringing within the teachings and traditions of that sect had a decisive influence on his career. After education at home he was articled to an apothecary, but was soon drawn to medicine. He began his studies by spending a year on the wards at the United Hospitals of St Thomas' and Guy's before entering the medical school at Edinburgh.

He qualified in 1823, having taken a year out to visit Paris, where he met Laënnec. Hodgkin was an early advocate of Laënnec's stethoscope, bringing the new instrument to England. While still a student, he delivered a lecture on the stethoscope at a meeting of the Guy's Hospital Physical Society, where it was initially received with scepticism.

In 1825 Hodgkin was appointed Lecturer in Morbid Anatomy and the first curator of the anatomy museum (now the Gordon Museum, see page 15) which was established at this time at Guy's Hospital Medical School. He seized the opportunities the post offered, giving the first systematic lectures on morbid anatomy in England and performing autopsies. In 1829 he catalogued the museum's contents, demonstrating the influence of disease on the body's organs and tissues. His work at Guy's was to earn him his reputation as one of the leading pathologists of his time.

Hodgkin's most important contributions to pathology were his original observations on the biconcave shape of red blood cells, the striation of voluntary muscle, incompetence of the aortic valve (20 years before Sir Dominic John Corrigan whose name is associated with Corrigan's pulse) and acute appendicitis. However his name is most widely

Thomas Hodgkin's stethoscope is on display in the Gordon Museum. Hodgkin encountered the new instrument in Paris and presented a paper on its use to the Guy's Hospital Physical Society in 1822.

recognized through his eponymous disease. In 1832 he published *On Some Morbid Appearances of the Absorbent Glands and Spleen*, a description of seven cases of enlargement of the lymph glands and spleen. Hodgkin's name was attached to this condition by Guy's physician, Samuel Wilks (1824-1911) who, making similar, independent observations in 1865, became aware of Hodgkin's work. We now know that Hodgkin's seven cases included tuberculosis as well as Hodgkin's and non-Hodgkin's lymphoma.

In 1837 Hodgkin failed to be appointed to the post of assistant physician at Guy's, in part or wholly due to his Quaker and reformist views on slavery, medical education and discrimination against non-Anglicans. He resigned his post and practised privately, also teaching at St Thomas' Hospital Medical School for a short while.

During his remaining years he travelled widely as personal physician and friend of the philanthropist Sir Moses Montefiore. Although married, he had no children, but the family name lived on through his brother, of whom Sir Alan Hodgkin, Nobel laureate for Medicine in 1963, was a direct descendant.

This specimen, which Hodgkin studied, shows a portion of the abdomen from a case of Hodgkin's disease. Thomas B was admitted with a two year history of enlarged glands in the neck axillae and groins with progressive emaciation. Autopsy revealed mediastinal and abdominal lymph node enlargement. The specimen, part of the Gordon Museum collection, shows the aorta encased in enlarged lymph nodes.

4769

Thomas Addison

Thomas Addison (1795-1860) was the son of a grocer, and was educated at Newcastle. He qualified in Edinburgh in 1815 then moved to London to start his practice. In 1817 he enrolled as a pupil physician at Guy's and was eventually appointed physician in 1837. For a period he was a joint lecturer with Richard Bright, with whom he was to write the well known textbook, *Elements of the Practice of Medicine*.

Addison's name is attached to two diseases, pernicious anaemia (Addisonian anaemia) and adrenal insufficiency (Addison's disease). At the outset he did not distinguish between them, until his finding of postmortem abnormalities in the adrenal glands made him realize that disease of the adrenals could not be related to the patients with anaemia. He described

eleven cases in *On the Constitutional and Local Effects of Disease of the Suprarenal Capsules* (1855). Interestingly, Bright had previously described one of the cases, noting the same features as Addison, but had failed to make the connection between the clinical and pathological features.

Addison made several other original descriptions: of the pathology of pneumonia (showing that inflammation was actually in the airways, in the alveoli, and not confined to the interstitium), and of skin disorders such as xanthoma diabeticorum, morphea, and xanthomata in hyperlipidaemia. His lifelong interest in dermatology led him to found the department of skin diseases at Guy's in 1824. Wax models of skin disorders which he commissioned are still in the Gordon Museum today (pictured below).

Addison was renowned as a teacher, but was plagued by depression. He retired in 1860, unable to work, and a few months later committed suicide.

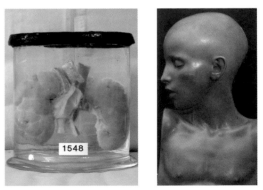

1548

One of Thomas Addison's original cases of his eponymous disease. On the **right** is a wax model by Joseph Towne of Robert B, age 12, admitted with abdominal pain, vomiting and discoloration of the skin. He died eight months later. At autopsy the only abnormalities were the skin colour and the adrenal glands shown on the **left** which were converted into fibrocaseous material. Microscopy showed giant cells indicating tuberculosis, a common cause of Addison's disease at the time. Both specimen and model are on display in the Gordon museum.

Richard Bright

Richard Bright (1789-1858) was born into a wealthy family which provided him with an excellent education and also allowed him to make several trips abroad during which he made various scientific, though not medical, observations.

He studied medicine at Edinburgh, Guy's and Cambridge (briefly), qualifying from Edinburgh in 1813. He settled and began to practise in London and was appointed physician at Guy's in 1844.

In his studies of morbid anatomy Bright was inspired by the surgeon and anatomy teacher Astley Cooper (see page 14). Between 1827 and 1836 Bright published three works describing and linking dropsy (oedema), urine which coagulated on heating, and postmortem changes in the kidney. His work clearly differentiated between renal and cardiac dropsy, ie

cardiac failure. He described subsets of postmortem renal changes and recognized that the clinical appearances in his patients could be due to a number of differing renal pathologies – a point that is now familiar, but was very advanced for its time. For his early observations, Bright is known as the 'father of nephrology'.

The description of Bright's disease, as it became known, is an outstanding example of careful clinical description and a 'chemical test' (albeit primitive) carried out during the patient's life, combined with postmortem findings.

Other original descriptions by Bright include pancreatic lesions in diabetes mellitus, laryngeal tuberculosis, pneumonia in whooping cough and unilateral convulsions associated with cerebral lesions.

Bright insisted on students accompanying him on his ward rounds and taking specimens of blood and urine for analysis and description, and established the first clinical investigation unit on the wards at Guy's.

He retired from Guy's in 1844 due to ill health, but continued in private practice. He died in 1858 from aortic valve disease, a diagnosis he himself had made several years earlier.

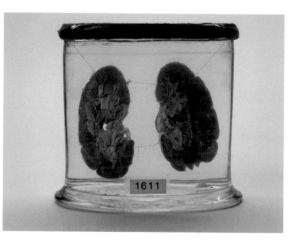

Above: A sectioned kidney from one of Richard Bright's original cases. Mary B, aged 34, was admitted with proteinuria of five year's duration. She died in a fit, and at autopsy the heart was healthy and of moderate size. The kidney is of normal size and has a granular surface. Histologically there is interstitial fibrosis and destruction of the glomeruli. The specimen is on display in the Gordon Museum.

The impact Hodgkin, Addison and Bright had on science and medicine in the nineteenth century did much to create the reputation of the medical school. The concentration of writings and lectures by these three physicians, produced over a relatively short period and from a single institution, was enormous. Their contributions are commemorated to this day in the naming of the Bright and Addison wards in Guy's Hospital and the Hodgkin Building, a centre for research and teaching, at the Guy's Campus.

Sir John Randall FRS
(1905-1984)

James Frederic Danielli
FRS (1911-1984)

Maurice Wilkins CBE FRS
(1916-2004)

Jean Hanson FRS
(1919-1973)

Robert Simmons FRS
(b 1938)

The cell: dissecting the new anatomy

Understanding how the body's cells work and communicate is central to our understanding of disease and has been a major focus of research at King's for several decades. It is 60 years since John Randall established the Biophysics Unit; the venue for the seminal works of Jean Hanson and Maurice Wilkins.

From the outset, scientists working in the unit sought and developed technologies based on physics to study biological problems; an aim that continues today. Jean Hanson (1919-1973) was one of the unit's first pioneers. She used the newly developed electron microscope to describe the sliding motion of muscle filaments, and later became King's first female Fellow of the Royal Society. Since then, King's has maintained its position at the forefront of cell biology research, applying a range of advanced techniques to study complex cellular functions and to shed light on disease mechanisms.

Randall and the Biophysics Unit at King's

Biophysics began at King's in 1946 when Sir John Randall became Wheatstone Professor of Physics and founding director of the newly established MRC Biophysics Research Unit. He developed a wide ranging research programme that involved physicists, biologists and biochemists and employed state-of-the-art equipment, such as the electron microscope. New types of light microscopes were being employed to study muscle contraction and at the same time X-ray diffraction studies were developed to study the 3D structure of molecules including the double helix model of DNA.

Before Randall's move to King's he worked at St Andrew's University with the physicist Maurice Wilkins (1916-2004), and when Randall started the Biophysics Research Unit, Wilkins joined him. Initially, Wilkins developed reflecting microscopes to study DNA within cells and viruses and measured the dry mass of cells using interference microscopes. He then went on to his X-ray diffraction studies of DNA and sperm heads for which he received a Nobel prize in 1962 (see page 25).

Jean Hanson (seated left) and colleagues in the MRC Biophysics Unit at King's in the 1950s.

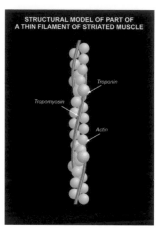

STRUCTURAL MODEL OF PART OF
A THIN FILAMENT OF STRIATED MUSCLE

Troponin

Tropomyosin

Actin

The helical arrangement of
actin molecules in the muscle
thin filament was first
demonstrated by electron
microscopy in the early 1960s
by Jean Hanson.

King's strength in muscle

Jean Hanson joined the Biophysics Research Unit in 1948 to study the structure of muscle and how it contracts. She was the first person to isolate myofibrils from rabbit skeletal muscle and make them contract *in vitro* in physiological salt solutions. This development marked the beginning of a new era of studies that allowed scientists to investigate the structural and biochemical properties of assemblies of molecules under controllable conditions.

In the early 1950s, Hanson went to the Massachusetts Institute of Technology, USA to learn how to use an electron microscope and it was there that, with HE Huxley, she made the seminal description of the sliding filament mechanism of muscle contraction. Hanson and Huxley had realized that it was overlapping arrays of actin and myosin filaments which were responsible for the characteristic appearance of striated muscle and which slide past one another during contraction. When Hanson returned to the Biophysics Unit she went on to demonstrate the existence of the double filament mechanism in a wide variety of muscle types and molecular aspects of contraction. Hanson became Professor of Biology in 1966 and the first woman from the College to become a Fellow of the Royal Society.

On Randall's retirement, Wilkins became Professor of Biophysics. The position was later held by Robert Simmons (b 1938) who, like Hanson, has contributed significantly to our understanding of muscle

contraction. With AF Huxley he developed methods to measure muscle mechanics. During the 1990s, whilst on sabbatical at Stanford University, USA, he developed a laser apparatus that allowed activity of the muscle protein myosin to be measured accurately.

Early models of cell membranes

During the time that Randall's unit was breaking new ground in understanding muscle contraction and the cell's inner workings, James Frederic Danielli (1911-1984) became Professor of Zoology at King's. He had begun working on the structure of the cell membrane in the early 1930s and developed new methods for measuring the cell's chemical components. Together with Hugh Davson, Danielli proposed the first generally accepted model of the cell membrane in 1935. They described cellular membranes as a sandwich of lipids covered on both sides with proteins. They later realised there were 'active patches' and protein lined pores within the membranes and these could help move certain chemicals across the membrane. Danielli's membrane model was later modified to the 'fluid-mosaic' model that proposes that the proteins are globular in arrangement and float within the lipid bilayer.

On the move – cell shape and motility

There are many protein receptors integrated into the cell's outer membrane that allow it to detect chemoattractant molecules around them and facilitate migration. Cell migration is a vital process in normal human development, wound healing and inflammatory immune responses. When the cell receives an attractive signal, receptors and energy releasing proteins become activated, and actin filaments are polymerized (a process regulated by a series of proteins) and this provides the force for the plasma membrane to change shape and for the cell to move.

Understanding this complex series of events will give insight into cancer metastasis, developmental defects, and defective healing. An example of this area of research at King's is the finding that the major actin-nucleating protein in white blood cells is absolutely required for movement of macrophages and dendritic cells. Lack of this protein causes the immune deficiency disease Wiskott-Aldrich syndrome. Because their leukocytes cannot respond normally to chemoattractants, a normal defence mechanism, patients suffer repeated severe infections.

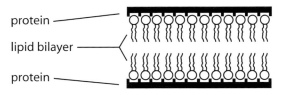

Danielli-Davson model of the cell membrane (1935).

protein ———

lipid bilayer ———

protein ———

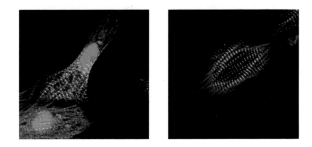

Cardiac muscle cells showing the distribution of titin, the largest human protein, stained red. Its size reflects its function as a signalling molecule along the length of the molecules which make up the sarcomere, the unit of contraction in muscle cell. On the **left** it is located in the sarcomere and the nucleus; on the **right** it is in the sarcomere of a contracting muscle cell.

The cytoskeleton – the cell's scaffolding

The cytoskeleton is a protein network that provides strength and resilience for cell membranes and plays an active role in the passage of protein complexes to reach the surface of the cell. Scientists at King's are studying the role of the cytoskeleton in cell movement and function. They use cutting edge imaging technology to study the locomotion of living cells and whilst studying the movement of malignant cells have found that signals passing between cells are critical for their movement.

Muscle cells of the heart are subjected to continuous mechanical stress. Their activity is controlled by calcium fluxes at the cell surface via protein complexes and as the cell beats these complexes must withstand the movement. The cytoskeleton plays a central role in this, the cytoskeletal proteins linking to the calcium handling apparatus as well as the contractile elements of the cell. Several proteins are involved and it is believed that defective forms of these proteins can lead to cardiomyopathy.

Unravelling the complexities of muscle

Muscle confers on animals one of their prime characteristics – mobility. Understanding the basis of muscle contraction and development is not only a challenge to physiologists, biochemists, physicists and geneticists but will also throw light on muscle diseases such as muscular dystrophy and cardiomyopathy. King's continues to use biophysical techniques to investigate mechanisms of muscle contraction and its regulation. The motor protein myosin that drives muscle contraction is studied at both the isolated cell and single molecule levels. Optical tweezers are employed to observe directly the interaction of a single molecule of myosin with actin, showing that myosin 'walks' with two molecular heads along the actin monomer (see next page).

In collaboration with the National Institute for Medical Research, researchers have developed a method for real-time measurements of the orientation of protein domains in cells. This approach bridges the gap between *in vitro* studies of protein structure and cellular studies of protein function and is being used to study the bending of the myosin molecule during contraction.

Another approach to understanding muscle is to study its embryonic development, and its abilities for growth and repair. In the mouse, two genes which regulate muscle and cartilage development (Meox1 and Meox2) have been identified. The next stage will be to identify the signals regulating these genes. Using the zebrafish as a model, work is in progress to understand how the basic programme for muscle development is modified to make individual muscles differ in size and contraction rate, and also how muscle repairs itself. With this knowledge the model can be used to test interventions to modify these functions and lead on to possible treatments for muscle disease.

An important area of research at King's is the mechanisms that organise the smallest contractile unit of striated muscle, the sarcomere, and how these crosstalk to mechanisms controlling muscle growth. Scientists at King's, in collaboration with the European Molecular Biology Group, have recently worked out how two muscle proteins – titin and telethonin – bond together. Titin is the largest of all human proteins and functions as a signalling molecule for the sarcomere. It bounces around rather like a bungee rope with hooks, making specific attachments to other proteins, including telethonin. Mutations in the titin gene can cause weakness of skeletal or cardiac muscle with serious consequences such as respiratory failure or heart failure.

Taking an imaging approach

Visualizing biological processes such as protein interactions between live cells in disease may give new ways of monitoring and interfering with these biological processes. Interacting molecules can exchange energy and this can be visualized using fluorescence and microscopy. New techniques for deep tissue imaging are being developed to provide 3D images of molecular events in thick biological tissue samples and small organisms.

Exploiting the membrane's potential

The importance of membrane proteins is reflected in the fact that over 70 per cent of the pharmaceutical products marketed today are targeted against them and include treatments for cancer, Parkinson's disease, migraine and epilepsy. Because of their biochemical characteristics, membrane proteins are notoriously difficult to study, so scientists at King's are developing a new bacterial expression system that will allow large-scale production of membrane proteins in bacterial cultures, eventually to be developed commercially in kit form.

Advances in our understanding of how membranes facilitate transfer of molecules are being exploited at King's. Scientists in the group are developing polymers and cationic vesicles that can be transferred across membranes as delivery vehicles for therapeutic genes. They are also using advanced neutron-scattering techniques to follow the course of the vectors' interaction with model membranes.

Embryonic development and stem cells

When an egg is fertilized, it is programmed to divide and the cells begin to differentiate into different cell types – a process called pattern formation. This is a closely regulated process that takes place in all animal embryos and is being studied by scientists at King's using the amphibian Xenopus.

Early stage embryos are also the source of embryonic stem cells and these have great therapeutic potential. The Stem Cell Laboratory at King's was the first in the UK to successfully derive human embryonic stem cells (hES) and to deposit them in the UK stem cell bank. One cell line has been derived from an embryo screened for a genetic mutation that accounts for 70 per cent of cystic fibrosis cases. This will be an important tool for studying the pathophysiology of this disease. The group also aims to produce therapeutically important somatic stem cell populations from hES cells, and is exploring the possibility of stem cell therapies for a range of disorders including Parkinson's, diabetes, and spinal cord damage.

The therapeutic potential of fetal and adult stem cells is also being studied. Scientists at King's have cultured fetal neural stem cells in large numbers in the laboratory and transferred them into the brains of mice who have suffered stroke. The cells allowed the mice to recover completely. Researchers are also using imaging technologies to monitor the passage of the injected cells within the body (see page 44).

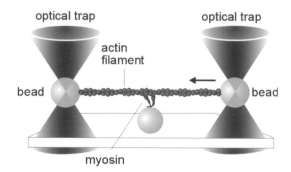

Studying the activity of a molecule of myosin. An actin filament is held taut and presented to a single myosin molecule. The actin filament is moved unidirectionally so the myosin molecule 'walks' along it; its activity is measured by the optical tweezers.

Teasing out the detail of muscle contraction

King's scientists are using an apparatus with laser beams known as 'optical tweezers' to measure the activity of the muscle protein myosin. The apparatus was developed by Robert Simmons and Steve Chu, one of the inventors of the tweezers, whilst Simmons was on sabbatical from King's at Stanford University in the US during the 1990s.

The tweezers work by moving a focused laser beam. If the object under study, such as a bead, moves away, the laser light is deflected and the particle is pushed in the opposite direction, back towards the focus. If the laser is moved the object moves, as with conventional tweezers. The tweezers can be set to alter their 'stiffness' so that the amount of force required to restore the object to the focus of the beam can be measured. The forces are similar to those exerted by the molecular motors that power muscle and actively transport material within cells.

Simmons studied movement of actin-coated beads on myosin-coated slides using the optical tweezers and found that actin-coated beads move in discrete steps of about 10nm. The technology is now being used to understand further the intricacies of the interactions between actin and myosin during muscle contraction.

Sir John Randall FRS
(1905-1984)

Maurice Wilkins CBE FRS
(1916-2004)

Paul Polani FRS
(1914-2006)

Alec Stokes (1919-2003)

Rosalind Franklin
(1920-1958)

Raymond Gosling
(b 1926)

Herbert Wilson (b 1929)

King's, DNA & the continuing story

James Watson and Francis Crick's paper proposing a structure for DNA in 1953 was based on undeniably inspired model-building but published without their undertaking a single experiment. Instead, the experiments underpinning those models were undertaken over the previous three years in the newly-formed Medical Research Council Biophysics Unit of King's College London.

The discovery that DNA is a double helix and that this structure comprises the hereditary material of living cellular organisms is perhaps the most momentous of our era. The insight that the discovery provided into how human characteristics arise from our individual genes created a veritable super-highway of research, ushering in gene therapy for inherited diseases and culminating in the sequencing of the human genome. The discovery also paved the way for a whole new arena of human endeavour, the biotechnology industry.

The prime movers in obtaining the data at King's were Maurice Wilkins (1916-2004), who had commenced pilot studies on the use of X-rays to analyse DNA structure, and Rosalind Franklin (1920-1958), who advanced the X-ray resolution of DNA structure to a new level of clarity and sophistication.

Wilkins studied physics at Cambridge then in John Randall's (1905-1984) department at the University of Birmingham. In his early years his work was involved with the Second World War, culminating in the Manhattan atomic bomb project. Partly as a reaction to the results in Japan and continuing threat to human life, he was attracted to biophysics, so that he could apply his knowledge to a more useful and intellectually attractive field. He teamed up with Randall again, first at St Andrew's and then at King's when Randall was invited to head the new MRC Biophysics Unit in 1946. This unit broke fresh ground, being the first to bring biologists, physicists and chemists together to study biological problems.

At that time it was not generally accepted that DNA was the cell's genetic material, but Randall and Wilkins, persuaded that it was, pressed ahead to

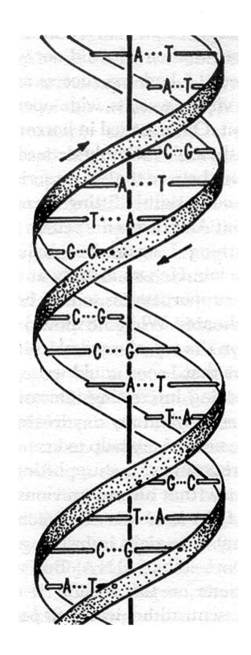

A schematic drawing showing the double helix structure of DNA.

With Ray Gosling, Rosalind Franklin (**left**) refined the process of X-ray diffraction at King's. By finding ways of increasing the humidity of the DNA fibres during the process, they produced sharper diffraction images in which a very well-defined pattern could be observed. Franklin died in 1958, aged 37.

Maurice Wilkins (**right**) with one of the cameras he developed for X-ray diffraction studies. He received the Nobel prize in 1962 with James Watson and Francis Crick for the discovery of the structure of DNA.

examine its structure by X-ray diffraction. Wilkins, working with a PhD student Raymond Gosling (b 1926), later Professor of Physics in Medicine at Guy's, obtained in 1950 the first clear X-ray diffraction pattern of DNA. Their colleague Alec Stokes (1919-2003), a physicist and mathematician, deduced that this pattern was due to a helical structure.

In this same year Randall invited Rosalind Franklin to join the unit and study the structure of DNA. Aged 30, Franklin already had a reputation as an excellent scientist; she had graduated from Cambridge in chemistry, then pursued significant work on the microstructure of graphite and coal before spending three years in Paris gaining extensive experience in X-ray diffraction. Franklin joining King's certainly strengthened the DNA project, but not entirely through the forging of a single team as she and Wilkins, although discussing their results, regarded themselves as working on separate programmes.

Franklin took over the supervision of Gosling's PhD thesis and they found DNA to have two forms – 'A' and 'B' – depending on water content, and with different diffraction patterns, 'A' being the form already characterized by Wilkins and Gosling. Meanwhile Crick and Watson were building models of DNA structure at Cambridge, there being a continual exchange of information between the two institutions. No model had yet satisfied the complex and expanding information on DNA's 3D structure and its chemical composition. In early 1953 Wilkins

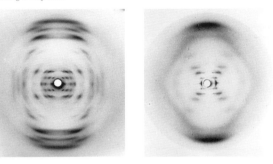

An X-ray diffraction image of the 'B' form of DNA taken by Frankin and Gosling in May 1952.

An X-ray diffraction pattern showing the 'A' form of DNA.

showed Watson a picture of 'B' DNA from Franklin's work, seemingly without her knowing, but Wilkins believing that the information was communal. Shortly afterwards the Cambridge group received the MRC's report on its site visit (December 1952) to Randall's department. The new information led Crick and Watson to a further model which was viewed by Wilkins in March 1953 and recognized by him to accord with his and Franklin's work, yet giving him new insight to DNA's structure too. These events took place against the background of Franklin's imminent departure to Birkbeck College, where she was planning to change her work to the structure of tobacco mosaic virus.

The latest Cambridge model was the basis of the famous publication by Watson and Crick in *Nature*, April 1953, proposing the structure of DNA, which appeared as a sequence of three papers on DNA (the other two being by Wilkins, Stokes and Wilson, and Franklin and Gosling, on the X-ray diffraction data and structural conclusions of DNA preparations).

Other proposals for the structure of DNA were being made, and over the next seven years Wilkins and his colleague, Herbert Wilson (b 1929), a physicist specialising in X-ray diffraction, undertook further structural studies to confirm Watson and Crick's proposed structure of the double helix. For this work and his earlier studies on DNA, Wilkins shared with Crick and Watson the Nobel Prize for Medicine or Physiology in 1962. Franklin had died from cancer in 1957; the Nobel prize is not awarded posthumously and

DNA fibres mounted on a cork and a paperclip by Wilkins for X-ray diffraction.

is not shared between more than three laureates. Readers of the autobiographies or biographies of the main contributors to the unravelling of DNA and of the many accounts of the sequence of events will recognize not only the brevity of the above account, but also Adrian Hayday's (King's Professor of Immunobiology) comment that 'the story is mired in utterly compelling complexity'. It is perhaps better to focus on the facts: the combination of work eventually resulting in the discovery of DNA's structure and function was recognized at the time by *Nature* in publishing the three seminal papers back to back; the award of the Nobel Prize, which by its constitution can recognize groups as much as individuals, to the three laureates; and above all to acknowledge the benefits already achieved and yet to come from the leap in understanding of heredity.

Building on new knowledge

This new knowledge was soon put to use with the foundation at Guy's of the Paediatric Research Unit by the Spastics Society in 1960. Its first director was Paul Polani (1914-2006) who shortly after became the first Prince Philip Professor of Paediatric Research. He graduated from Pisa in 1938 and came to the UK to start his career as a house surgeon at Lewisham Hospital. On the outbreak of the Second World War he joined the merchant navy, but was interned when Italy declared war on the UK in 1940. He was released, and found his way, as a locum, to the Evelina Children's Hospital,

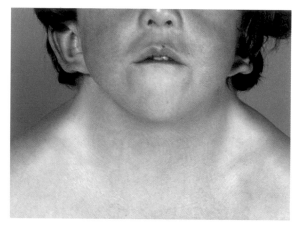

A case of Turner's syndrome which is demonstrated in the webbing of the neck. Paul Polani observed that the syndrome affected girls with a chromosomal abnormality which altered their sexual development.

where he stayed for six years, before moving to Guy's. From the beginning of his appointment Polani recognized that an understanding of genetics and its application to clinical observation and practice were fundamental to medicine, and especially paediatrics. At first interested in congenital heart disease, he noted that the incidence of aortic coarctation (a narrowing of the aorta) in a congenital disorder of girls, Turner's syndrome, was similar to that in normal boys (higher than in normal girls). Turner's syndrome affects 1 in 3,000 births with webbing of the neck, restricted growth and failed development at puberty, and congenital cardiovascular abnormalities, particularly coarctation of the aorta. Polani's observations on coarctation led him to think that the girls with Turner's syndrome might be genetically males. This was before the days of chromosomal analysis, but buccal smears on patients with Turner's syndrome showed that they did indeed have the chromatin pattern of males. He suggested that genetically they would not be XX (female) nor XY (male) but XO, and was later proven right. Polani was the first to indicate that a chromosomal

abnormality could produce a defect in sexual development, and suggested that others could occur, which is now known to be the case.

Other original observations Polani made were that an individual could have two populations of cells with different chromosomes, and the explanation of the familial form of Down's syndrome.

On his retirement in 1982 he was succeeded by Martin Bobrow (b 1938), who held the chair until moving to Cambridge in 1995. His tenure was marked by a change in emphasis from chromosomal analysis to molecular genetics. Genetic linkage was based on DNA markers and new techniques established for detection of mutations, with particular relevance for Duchenne muscular dystrophy, X-linked agammaglobulinaemia, Alport's syndrome and Tay-Sachs disease.

With the rising public concern over many of the implications of the expanding knowledge of genetics and DNA biology and its applications, Bobrow became an influential member of national committees and an authoritative voice on the current problems.

Research in genetic diseases has moved from mapping Mendelian disease-related genes in two directions. The first is studying the functions of genes and their products, and the related cell and molecular biology. The second direction is complex genetic disease – common diseases such as heart disease and cancer are not due to a single gene defect, but are related to genes which increase the individual's susceptibility. Identification of these genes has important implications for diagnosis, prognosis, prevention and therapy.

Cancer genetics

Breast cancer is one of the commonest malignancies affecting women in the UK; one in nine will develop it. Some patients with breast cancer have a gene – BRCA1 – which predisposes to early-onset familial cancer of the breast and ovary. This gene gives a lifetime risk of 70 per cent for breast and 40 per cent for ovarian cancer.

BRCA1 has several functions; one is to form a complex with two other proteins to form an enzyme, ubiquitin ligase, which repairs DNA. Work at King's has shown that most mutations in BRCA1 cause the enzyme to be inactive and so fail to repair DNA. However screening of many women with breast cancer has revealed many missense mutations whose effect is entirely unknown, raising serious difficulties in counselling the families. It was therefore important to study in detail these missense mutations; reproducing them in the protein complex has shown several different interactions between the three proteins and also loss of ubiquitin ligase activity in many of them. A functional assay for these mutations is being developed which will make the clinical counselling of the affected individuals more effective.

King's is also studying acute promyelocytic leukaemia (APL), one of the commonest forms of acute myeloid leukaemia. APL is unique in that treatment with all-trans retinoic acid usually leads to complete remission in the short term (and long term with consolidation chemotherapy). The genetic fault is a translocation between chromosomes 15 and 17 to form a new fusion gene which produces a fusion oncogene (PML-RARa).

The mechanisms causing translocation are poorly understood, but a clue has come from APL secondary to treatment with mitoxantrone in patients with breast cancer – an example of treatment-related leukaemia, increasingly common following successful cancer therapy. Mitoxantrone is a cytotoxic drug which disrupts DNA by inhibiting topoisomerase, which regulates the coiling, transcription and replication of DNA. In these patients with secondary APL the translocation breakpoints were clustered on chromosome 15 at a site where topoisomerase inhibitors act, so implicating mitoxantrone in causing the secondary APL. This information is leading to studies to define the translocation(s) in primary APL.

Monitoring patients with cancer for relapse is a vital part of their management and the same group at King's has developed a method (real time PCR) for APL which can detect one cell in 10,000, giving early warning of relapse and allowing treatment to recommence well before clinical relapse shows.

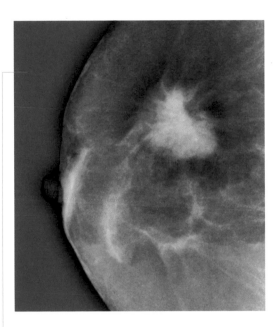

Mammogram of a woman's breast that contains a cancerous tumour (white). King's is leading research on identifying key genes which influence the development of breast cancer. This type of malignancy is the most common cause of cancer death in women.

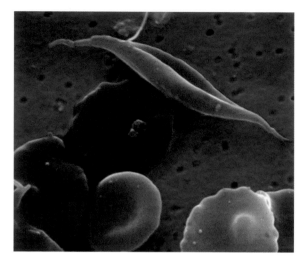

Single gene diseases

Examples of single gene diseases to which King's is making a contribution in understanding are Huntington's disease and sickle cell disease.

Huntington's disease presents in people between 30 and 50 years old with progressive dementia and abnormal and uncontrollable limb movements. The gene, an autosomal dominant and its product, huntingtin, have been identified. Work at King's has developed a transgenic mouse model to understand pathogenesis and to evaluate treatments. Aggregates of huntingtin in the brain are related to cell damage and death and the mouse model is being used to examine methods of reducing these aggregates.

Sickle cell disease (SCD) is one of the inherited disorders of red blood cells involving abnormal haemoglobin production – the commonest genetic disorders worldwide. SCD is due to an autosomal recessive gene and occurs mainly in African and Afro-Caribbean people; it has a particular relevance for King's and its partner hospitals in South East London

owing to the large number of these ethnic minorities in the local population. The disorder is caused by the production of a defective form of haemoglobin, HbS. Red cells with HbS have a shortened life span; patients become anaemic and the red cells become sickle-shaped. This abnormal shape impairs red cells' passage through small blood vessels, with sludging, thrombosis and reduced blood supply as consequences.

Normally, haemoglobin production switches from the fetal form, HbF, to the adult form, HbA, with a residual continuing production of HbF. In patients with SCD the greater the level of residual HbF, the less the severity of SCD, so ways to augment HbF production, which is beneficial, are being sought. The approach at King's has been to search for genes regulating HbF production and two candidates have been identified on different chromosomes; once accurately defined, upregulating these genes offers a possible new treatment.

Complex gene disease

One group of diseases being examined at King's is inflammatory bowel disease – Crohn's disease and ulcerative colitis. Two susceptibility genes have been identified. One on chromosome 16 increases the risk of Crohn's disease by a factor of three in the heterozygote and a factor of 27 in the homozygote and is specific for ileal Crohn's disease. The second gene also confers susceptibility to Crohn's and its early

In 1993 on the 40th anniversary of the discovery of the structure of DNA, King's erected a special plaque at the Strand Campus to mark the College's contribution to the discovery.
From left: Raymond Gosling, Herbert Wilson, Maurice Wilkins and Alec Stokes.

onset but, interestingly, only if mutations are present in the first gene, suggesting the two interact in a common pathway.

King's is taking part in an £8.6 million Wellcome Trust Case Control Consortium to identify susceptibility genes for common disorders, coordinating with Cambridge the study of inflammatory bowel disease. The others are Types 1 and 2 diabetes, hypertension, coronary heart disease, rheumatoid arthritis, tuberculosis and bipolar disorder.

Peter Gorer FRS
(1907-1961)

A *fundamental discovery in immunology:* Peter Gorer & murine H-2

Peter Gorer's discovery of murine H-2 lies at the heart of cellular immunology, and provides a basis for understanding the immune response to infections, tumours, and transplanted organs, as well as autoimmune disease.

His legacy continues in the Division of Immunology, Infection and Inflammatory Disease, which conducts research over a wide range of interests. This research is being translated into understanding and treating many different conditions ranging from Type 1 diabetes, transplantation, rheumatoid arthritis and multiple sclerosis to HIV infection.

A specific cellular response

With Pasteur's rationalisation of Jenner's pox prophylaxis (Pasteur termed it vaccination in honour of Jenner), it became clear that the body possessed protective mechanisms to fight the microbes that Koch and colleagues proved to be the causes of myriad diseases. The mechanism of protection was tackled by Kitasato and von Behring, who was awarded the Nobel Prize in 1901 for characterisation of antibodies in the humor; and by Metchnikoff, who,

working with single-cell organisms and starfish larvae, demonstrated that cells that he termed macrophages could engulf and digest microbes. Thus, there appeared to be not one but several distinct mechanisms of immunological protection. However, there was a critical distinction between the humoral and cellular responses as described by these great pioneers. Whereas Kitasato and von Behring showed that the antibodies were highly pathogen-specific, and varied among individuals according to prior infections, macrophages attack a broad range of microbes, and are broadly similar in all individuals from birth to death. In short, they represent an innate response, whereas the antibodies reflect pathogen-specific adaptations to the burden of microbes that we confront in life. The question posed was whether there was a cellular component of the adaptive response, and if so, how it might work.

George Snell

Gorer sustained a powerful collaboration with George Snell at the Jackson Laboratory in Bar Harbor, Maine. Snell was later awarded the Nobel Prize for Physiology in 1980 for his work on histocompatability. In his acceptance speech he credited Peter Gorer, who died in 1961, as being the original discoverer of H-2.

A critical step along the way to answering this question was provided in London in the 1930s by Dr Peter Gorer (1907-1961) whose work transformed immunology. Gorer identified several determinants of tumour cells to which the immune systems of inoculated mice would react. Because he had the rare foresight to realise the importance of raising and using genetically identical mice for his studies, he deduced that the second determinant, H-2, was not a tumour-specific response, but a response of one strain of mouse to the cells of another. The relevant paper in 1937 is a tour-de-force of experimental reasoning, but its full significance was not recognised until well into the 1940s, by which time Gorer had been appointed Reader in Experimental Pathology at Guy's in 1947. Without teaching responsibility, and hence with almost total freedom to carry out research, Gorer sustained a powerful collaboration he had begun with George Snell at the Jackson Laboratory in Bar Harbor, Maine. Snell had initiated his own studies of the genetics of histo-compatibility, that began to mesh extraordinarily with work on the blood-typing of mice with tumours resistant to the immune response that Gorer undertook during a year's stay at Bar Harbor. Together they demonstrated that the histo-compatibility locus responsible for Snell's observations was one and the same as H-2 described by Gorer a decade earlier. A decade later, and the human equivalent of H-2, known as HLA, was characterised by Dausset, following which it was shown that the natural function of H-2/HLA is to bind to small fragments of microbes and present them for recognition to thymus-derived T-cells that compose the core of the cellular adaptive response. Hence, H-2 lies at the heart of cellular immunology, regulating the body's specific responses to infection, transplanted organs, and tumours, and, when awry, causing the body to attack its own tissues in autoimmune diseases such as Type 1 diabetes and multiple sclerosis, each of which is linked to genetic polymorphisms in H-2/HLA. Indeed, the whole science of tissue-typing that offers prognoses for transplant acceptance was born of Gorer's work.

Snell, whose work on histocompatibility was awarded the Nobel Prize for Physiology or Medicine in 1980, described Gorer's work in immunobiology as reinforcing his own discovery of H-2: 'Dr Peter Gorer was the original discoverer of H-2,' he said in his Nobel acceptance speech, 'and although my own identification of the complex was independent, our studies, once united, reinforced each other. Dr Gorer's untimely death (in 1961) was a tragic loss to his many friends and to this field of science.' Among them were several eminent researchers whom Gorer attracted to his research team at Guy's, including Ed Boyse, Bernard Amos and Gustavo Hoecker.

Promulgating the legacy

When a new research initiative in immunology was started at King's in 1999, it seemed only appropriate to name it the Peter Gorer Department of Immuno-biology. Shortly afterwards, the Department was able to move into state-of-the-art laboratories, opened by Archbishop Desmond Tutu in February 2004. The new facilities are an active hub where almost 80 scientists research topics at the interface of infection and immunity. Building on the foundation of Gorer's work, the Department is studying a second type of T-cell. Unlike conventional T-cells, these 'gamma delta' T-cells do not engage H-2/HLA. This led to the

hypothesis of the existence of a parallel system of
recognition that may be particularly important in the
response to certain infections, such as cytomegalovirus
(which poses a major problem in the transplant clinic)
and tumours. In collaboration with colleagues at Yale,
gamma delta T-cells were unequivocally shown to be
an essential component of the mouse immune
response to chemically-induced cancer.

Broadening the legacy

Together with five other departments, the Peter Gorer
Department of Immunobiology forms the Division of
Immunology, Infection and Inflammatory Disease
(DIIID), whose goal is to understand the interplay
between our immune systems and the infections,
tumours, and autoimmune problems that afflict us.
To this end, DIIID undertakes research across a broad
spectrum of interests – from the adaptive response of
B cells in the human gut; through characterising T-cell
memory at the molecular level, to the description of
the T-cells that promote Type 1 diabetes. Research
also spans the basic science laboratory, through the
clinical laboratory and practice to the statistical
assessment of clinical trial design in rheumatoid
arthritis. The emphasis is on the translation of the
discovery of important molecules and their roles into
clinical applications. For example, a vaccine has been
devised that may promote the transition of pathogenic
T-cells specific for the pancreas in Type 1 diabetes,
into protective cells that specifically suppress T-cells
attacking the pancreas which have been identified in
unafflicted siblings (see page 88).

Large scale immune problems

Research in the departments of DIIID in the fields of
infection, renal medicine, and neuroimmunology are
described in chapters 14, 19 and 6 respectively. The
Department of Rheumatology is featured here as a
further example of dissecting T-cell function in a
human disease.

The Department's main focus is rheumatoid
arthritis (RA), among the most common of all autoimmune diseases, affecting more than 350,000 people
in the UK alone, and several million worldwide. While
the management of RA has recently been
revolutionised by drugs such as infliximab that block
the effects of the inflammatory agent, tumour necrosis
factor-alpha, there is still scant understanding of its
pathogenesis, essential to the development of disease-
specific rather than generally immuno-suppressive
therapies.

Rheumatology research at King's also has a great
legacy. Alfred Baring Garrod (1819-1907), Professor of
Materia Medica and Therapeutics at King's in 1863,
described the phenotypes of chronic arthritis and first

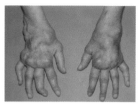
Hands of a patient with rheumatoid arthritis. There is severe deformity caused by joint destruction and inevitable disability.

coined the term 'rheumatoid arthritis'. He also discovered the abnormal uric acid metabolism in gout. Within DIIID, the current Department of Rheumatology integrates basic and clinical research, focussing on how T-cells get into the joints, and determining ways in which these may also be converted into protective regulatory cells. In parallel, DIIID has sponsored a new strand of research investigating how mesenchymal stem cells may be provoked *in situ* to repair damaged joints. The intention is to couple such technology to highly specific anti-inflammatory regimens to effect complete rehabilitation of RA patients.

Drug and non-drug therapies are being evaluated using clinical trials and systematic reviews as well as correlating patient outcomes with novel genetic markers. The aim is to improve patient care by involving patients in their own treatment and introducing a 'total quality care' strategy. As such, the Clinical Trials Unit links basic research with outcomes research and currently acts as the coordinating centre for two international and three national trials, all aimed at improving treatment of inflammatory rheumatic diseases.

Immunobiology not immunology

Assigning the name Immunobiology rather than Immunology to the new Peter Gorer Department, recognises the breadth of science that necessarily underpins contemporary progress in immunology.

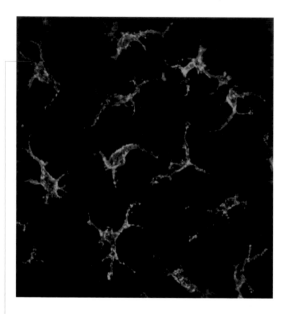
Gamma-delta T-cells. This sub-set of lymphocytes functions differently to other T-cells and provides 'alternative' protection against infections and tumours.

Researchers look not only at immune function but at the development of the immune system. One recent study unexpectedly showed that the cytokine, lymphotoxin, acts as a messenger co-ordinating the development of conventional T-cells with that of gamma delta T-cells.

Seemingly very basic research using cellular biochemistry and molecular biology to characterise ubiquitination, the process of tagging proteins for break-down, and proteolysis (the break-down process itself) may have an unexpectedly rapid pay-off in the finding that such processes appear to malfunction in Sezary syndrome, a variant of a cutaneous T-cell lymphoma. Such research highlights the cross-talk of DIIID with other units at King's, such as the St John's Institute of Dermatology, which likewise supports a key collaboration on the immunological underpinnings of psoriasis. Recent genetic data from the Division of Genetics and Molecular Medicine points to a susceptibility to psoriasis on a region of the genome in and around HLA-C. Thus, less than 100 years after his birth, Peter Gorer's extraordinary insights still illuminate the very modern facilities that support today's research at King's. The goal of that research is to scrutinise perceived wisdom in biomedicine; to develop and test novel hypotheses; and to advance our understanding of the basic causes of a wide range of diseases.

Robert Bentley Todd FRS (1809-1860)

John Louis William Thudichum (1829-1901)

Sir David Ferrier FRS (1843-1928)

Sir Charles Scott Sherrington FRS (1857-1952)

Murray Falconer (1910-1977)

David Marsden FRS (1938-1998)

Peter Baker FRS (1939-1987)

The mind & body interface: developments in neuroscience

Until the mid-nineteenth century there was much confusion about the nature of disorders of the mind and the cause and effect of neurological problems such as paralysis.

There were 'nervous diseases' or 'neuroses', including madness, which in retrospect included all of modern neurology and psychiatry. In the nineteenth century the advances made in neuroanatomy and neuropathology laid the foundations of modern neurology as more and more 'neuroses' were found to have a pathological basis. Physicians at the hospitals connected with King's College London made outstanding contributions to the new disciplines of neurology and neuroscience.

Foremost among them was Robert Bentley Todd (1809-1860) appointed at the age of 27 to the chair of Physiology and Morbid Anatomy at King's in 1836. He played three important roles aside from his work in neurology; founding in 1840 King's College Hospital of which he became an outstanding physician; pioneering educational reforms which turned medical students from apprentices into university graduates; and transforming the fortunes and reputation of King's College Medical School, of which he became the first Dean in 1842.

Todd is best remembered for his description of transient paralysis after an epileptic fit – Todd's paralysis – but this is a small part of his contributions to neurology and neuroscience. He was the first to recognize the functions of the posterior columns of the spinal cord, the concept of sensory (afferent) and motor (efferent) nerves and to give an account of the syphilitic disease of the spinal cord, *tabes dorsalis*.

Todd was the first to apply the concepts of his contemporary Michael Faraday of the polar forces of electricity and magnetism to the brain, laying the foundations of our modern understanding of the electrical basis of brain activity and developing the first electrical theory of epilepsy.

The other outstanding nineteenth-century King's neuroscientist and physician was David Ferrier (1843-1928). Primarily a neurophysiologist, he was appointed to the chair of Forensic Medicine in 1872 and then of Pathology in 1879. His great achievement was, with Hughlings Jackson, to map the localisation in the cortex of the brain of its motor, sensory, auditory and

Thudichum – father of neurochemistry

John Louis William Thudichum is regarded as the 'father of neurochemistry'.

Upon his appointment to St Thomas' as Physician in 1871, J Liepig, President of the Royal Academy of Science, wrote to Thudichum on his eminent suitability: 'True practice always grows out of the ground of science and a practising doctor who cultivates and advances his science is far superior. You have always zealously worked to enrich the field of medicine through scientific investigation without renouncing practical activity in which you have gained as many and as gratifying successes'.

visual functions. Their work led to the ability to localize resectable lesions to open up the field of neurosurgery.

The chemical connection

Studies of the brain's chemistry were conducted by John Louis William Thudichum (1829-1901), appointed lecturer and first director of a new laboratory of chemistry and pathology at St Thomas' Hospital medical school in 1865. He was a pioneer in spectroscopy and used his skills on biological materials, in particular brain tissue, to analyse their chemistry. He identified sulfatides, phosphatides and cerebrosides, naming several, such as sphingomyelin, and published his systematic studies of brain chemistry in 1874, albeit to great criticism. Unperturbed, Thudichum continued his research into physiological chemistry, making numerous important discoveries. He defined the effects of endogenous toxins on the brain and their role in illness. He did not confine his work to the brain but also studied gallstones, urine, vitamins and even wine. Today, Thudichum's work has outshone the criticism and he is regarded as the 'father of neurochemistry'.

Clinical neurology

Building on the developments in neuroanatomy and neuroscience, a period of fruitful clinical observations followed in the early twentieth century and subsequently. The earliest of these was by Kinnier

Wilson (1874-1937) appointed to King's as the first head in the UK of a medical school department of neurology. By the time of his appointment he was already famous for his description of his eponymous disease, a combination of involuntary movements, rigidity, dysarthria and cirrhosis of the liver (also known as lenticular degeneration). He noted its association with lesions in the brain's basal ganglia and was able to clarify that these structures were related to control of tone, movement and motor control.

MacDonald Critchley (1900-1997) was a junior colleague of Wilson's at King's. He particularly studied the cerebral function of the parietal lobes and the brain's use and perception of language. Charles Symonds (1890-1978) was appointed the first neurologist to Guy's in 1920 with specialism in vascular disorders of the nervous system, and the neurological basis of mental disorders. Ross Russell was a neurologist at St Thomas' Hospital and made notable observations on cerebrovascular disease and neuro-ophthalmology.

Surgery for epilepsy

The use of neurosurgery in treating epilepsy dated back to the nineteenth century, and perhaps into antiquity in the art of trepanning. It was during the post-war period that the electroencephalogram became available for routine clinical use and as such allowed the 'location' of seizures to be identified, so

David Marsden was one of the most outstanding neurologists of his time. His legacy was widespread in neuroscience and clinical neurology, delivered in three major academic posts - Professor of Neurology at The Institute of Psychiatry and King's College Hospital School of Medicine, Professor of Clinical Neurology at The Institute of Neurology, and finally Dean of The Institute.

enabling targeted surgical intervention.

The appointment of Murray Falconer (1910-1977) as Director of Neurosurgery at Guy's Hospital in 1949 marked an extremely productive surgical programme for treating temporal lobe epilepsy resistant to antiepileptic drugs. Falconer developed new techniques for temporal lobectomy and collaborated with colleagues at the Institute of Psychiatry in detailed studies of the neuropsychiatry and neuropathology in postoperative patients.

Moving science

Movement disorders and clinical neuroscience were high on the agenda for David Marsden (1938-1998), who took the first professorial chair of neurology at the Institute of Psychiatry and held consultant appointments at both the Maudsley and King's College Hospitals. An outstanding personality, he established pioneering research programmes in neurophysiology and neuropharmacology. Among Marsden's most important contributions were his definition of the dystonias as neurological rather than psychiatric diseases and his description of the neurological effects of neuroleptic drugs. He also established the first specialist clinics in the UK for patients with Parkinson's disease and other movement disorders, and persuaded the Parkinson's disease Society to set up and fund a 'brain bank' at the Institute of Psychiatry that underpins much of the current research into this disease.

Notably named

King's has, it might be said, produced more than its share of eponymous diseases. In 1956, Brian McArdle in the Chemical Pathology Department at Guy's Hospital Medical School made the seminal observations on the failure of lactate to rise in the ischaemic forearm which led to the description of phosphorylase deficiency now called McArdle's Disease: the first entry in the burgeoning textbook of metabolic muscle disorders.

Peripheral nervous system

Charles Scott Sherrington (1857-1952) was an influential contributor to the understanding of the peripheral nervous system, in particular reflex action. Most of his research was undertaken outside King's, but he completed his studies at St Thomas' in 1883 and became lecturer in physiology at St Thomas' in 1887. Sherrington's most important work was summarized in his Silliman lectures at Yale University in 1904, published in 1906 as: *The Integrative Action of the Nervous System*. In this, he united experimental data to provide a new perspective on nervous function, coordination, and connectivity. This work provided a firm basis of our current understanding of the nervous system and how it handles information. As Lord Adrian remarked, Sherrington's work 'opened up an entirely new chapter in the physiology of the central nervous system'.

Sir Charles Sherrington

Sir Charles Sherrington, Nobel laureate, and President of The Royal Society, made fundamental contributions to neuroscience which were compared to those of William Harvey to the circulation of the blood. As well as achieving the highest recognition for his scientific work he was a philosopher. His book *Man on Nature* was selected as one of the 100 outstanding modern British books at the Festival of Britain in 1951.

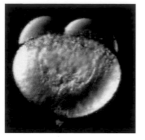

A zebra fish embryo, used for studying brain development. Zebra fish have a rapid rate of development, three days for a zebra fish being equal to three months for a human embryo; they are transparent so developmental changes are easily observed; a single fish can produce tens of thousands of embryos.

Important experimental contributions were made by Peter Baker (1939-1987) Professor of Physiology until his early death. He studied the role of intracellular ions in excitability of nerves, particularly calcium and sodium and coupling between the fluxes of these two ions, and also magnesium and phosphorus metabolism.

The Decade of the Brain – the 1990s – saw significant advances in understanding the development of the central and peripheral nervous systems. Brain function is highly susceptible to ageing with a consequent increase in acute and chronic brain disease as we grow older. As well as needing treatment for movement disorders, dementia and other neurodegenerative conditions, therapy to repair the central and peripheral cells of the nervous system is also urgently required.

Research at King's aims to understand the development and growth of the nervous system, how signals are transmitted within it, and how the regeneration of nerve cells can be induced. Clinical research complements this by exploring the pathology, genetics and treatment of a number of different conditions ranging from Alzheimer's disease to motor neurone disease.

The developing brain

The MRC Centre for Developmental Neurobiology focuses on the early events during brain development. This work leads into crucial areas impacting on clinical medicine. First, understanding the mechanisms leading to malformations in the brain and second, analyzing how the human nervous system's ability to regenerate after damage is so limited. Using a variety of models, such as the fruit fly and zebrafish, it combines gene discovery with functional analyses at molecular, biochemical, anatomical and physiological levels.

Signalling

The ability of neurones (the cells of the nervous system) to transmit impulses to each other across their synapses, or junctions, is at a premium for speed and complexity in the nervous system. Diseases at the synapses can arise through deficiencies or over-production of substances involved in transmission.

The King's Receptors and Signalling Group focuses on acute and chronic brain disease and the relief of symptoms through enhancement or suppression of synaptic activity. The effects of L-Dopa in Parkinson's disease and cholinesterase inhibitors in Alzheimer's, are well known examples of replacement therapy. In contrast, the phenomenon of 'excitotoxicity' in acute problems, such as stroke, head injury and epilepsy, involves damage to neurones by the neurotransmitters themselves. Treatment is aimed at glutamate suppression or modulating the effects of other chemicals in the signalling pathways.

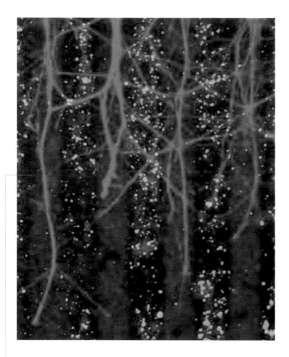

Nerve fibres growing on a molecular carpet. The MRC Centre for Developmental Neurobiology is deciphering the genetic instructions for building a brain.

Neurorestoration

An unmet need in neurological disease is to restore function to the damaged nervous system; the media often publicise acute spinal cord injury, but of course the whole nervous system would benefit from such treatment. Earlier work on this began with Frank Walsh, Professor of Experimental Pathology until he moved to the pharmaceutical industry in 1997. His interest was in the growth and regeneration of nerve cells and focussed on cell surface adhesion molecules which promote and inhibit growth. The aim of the Neurorestoration Group is to promote new connections between nerve cells where there have been breaks and another is to replace damaged neurones with new ones. New neurones may come from grafts into the damaged area or be generated by stimulating the differentiation of the body's own stem cells.

Clinical neurology

Diseases of the nervous system can be particularly distressing as they affect body functions such as movement, including speech and swallowing, control of bladder and bowel, and higher brain functions such as memory, thought processes and communication. The burden to patients, their families and carers, and the financial cost to the state through providing care and lost productivity is enormous. Much therapy is still only symptomatic, but advances in the understanding, particularly in genetics and molecular pathology, of these illnesses is now leading to possibilities for prevention and treatment. Work at King's is focused on several of these diseases.

Alzheimer's

Neurodegenerative diseases are an increasing burden on society as a result of current demographic change. The most common is Alzheimer's disease (AD), affecting 400,000 in the UK. Although present treatment improves symptoms for a short period in some patients, none slow the relentless degeneration in the brain. Understanding the molecular events in the diseased brain is essential to develop effective drugs. Microscopically AD is characterized by 'tangles' and 'plaques' in the brain related to excess deposits of two proteins, tau causing tangles and amyloid causing plaques. Tau is a normally occurring protein, but in AD contains an abnormal amount of phosphate which prevents its elimination from brain cells, causing their death. The excess phosphate content of tau has been shown to be caused by an enzyme, GSK3, which is found to be raised in AD patients.

Lithium, already well-known in psychiatric treatment, inhibits GSK3 and a trial of this drug for AD is underway at King's. On a more general note for the population at large, the inevitable deterioration of

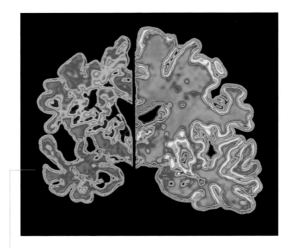

Two brain scans showing a patient with Alzheimer's disease on the left and a normal subject on the right, demonstrating the loss of brain tissue. The Alzheimer's disease brain is considerably shrunken, due to the degeneration and death of nerve cells. One in five people over the age of 85 in the UK have Alzheimer's disease.

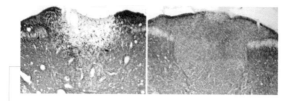

memory and concentration with ageing has been shown to be slowed by the antioxidant vitamins A, C and E and isoflavones, natural plant oestrogens found in soya.

Multiple sclerosis

Multiple sclerosis (MS) is one of the commonest chronic neurogical diseases, affecting 85,000 people in the UK. It still lacks a definitive treatment. However in a model of MS a remarkable degree of protection from degeneration has been found by using flecainide, a sodium-channel blocker. This work has led to a clinical trial starting in 2005 of this drug in patients with secondary progressive multiple sclerosis.

Attention has also focused on the role of nitric oxide in MS in causing damage to the axons. It is found in high concentrations in the lesions of MS, and inhibitors of its action could open a new avenue of treatment.

Motor neurone disease

Motor neurone disease (MND) causes progressive muscle wasting due to degeneration of the motor neurones (the nerve cells controlling muscle movement) which activate the body's muscles. Patients suffer muscular paralysis affecting limbs, breathing and swallowing. It affects 5,000 people in the UK and causes 1,200 deaths yearly (the average survival is around two to three years). The reason for the degeneration is unknown but work at King's has led to a number of new findings.

Patients with multiple sclerosis can experience permanent loss of function due to the degeneration of large numbers of nerve fibres. No current therapy is known to protect fibres, but research indicates that sodium channel blocking drugs can be effective. The photographs show cross-sections through the spinal cord in which nerve fibres have been labelled brown. On the left can be seen a pale area in which nearly all nerve fibres have degenerated due to the disease process. On the right, nearly all the nerve fibres have been protected by therapy with a flecainide sodium channel blocking agent, despite the presence of the disease. Clinical trials began in 2005, based on these observations.

Some cases of MND are familial and a new locus on chromosome 16 has recently been identified and is being mapped. In five to ten per cent of patients MND develops due to a mutation in the gene SOD1. Brain scans are being used to compare the pattern of damage in these patients with that in the usual MND in which no cause has been identified; similarities and differences should help understand why and how the neurones degenerate. Using a transgenic mouse model of MND, a series of disease-associated proteins has been found in the animals' cerebrospinal fluid and these are now being sought in patients.

Stem cell research offers another method to explore the degeneration in MND cells. In collaboration with the Roslin Institute stem cells are being used to produce motor neurone cells carrying defective genes causing MND. Studying these cells will help define the cellular events leading to their degeneration, and they can also be used to screen drugs for their ability to prevent MND. Progress along these lines has led to clinical trials of various drugs, resulting in the only approved drug to date for MND, riluzole.

Peripheral nerve disease

Diseases affecting the peripheral nerves – those directly supplying muscles for movement and skin and for sensation – have many different causes. The commonest in the UK now is diabetes. A much rarer form with a particular interest at King's is Guillain-Barré syndrome, which is thought to have an autoimmune basis. Recent work has shown that infection due to Haemophilus influenzae is a cause of the disease in a proportion of cases. A separate immunological study has shown antibodies present in some patients to recombinant human myelin peptides.

Michael Maisey (b 1939)

Imaging: increasing the power to see within

The discovery of X-rays in 1895 by Wilhelm Röntgen heralded a leap in diagnostic ability which immediately touched every branch of medicine. Since that time the hospitals associated with King's have rapidly assimilated the new techniques in imaging and King's itself has contributed with the founding of an academic department in the 1970s.

After Röntgen's discovery it was St Thomas' Hospital to be first off the mark, taking the first X-ray pictures in a London hospital. Among these is an X-ray of the hand of a St Thomas' medical student showing a fracture of the head and neck of the fifth metacarpal bone.

Less auspicious was the X-ray imaging of Tutankhamen's mummy which took place at St Thomas' in 1922; the radiologist, Archibald Reid, died a year later, adding fuel to the supposed curse on those who opened the tomb or disturbed its contents.

An important practical advance in the 1890s was the design of a new form of Crookes' tube (the vacuum tube designed by William Crooke, a British physicist, used by Röntgen to produce the original X-rays) by a Mr Jackson of King's College. His new design focused the X-rays, which allowed images to be taken in five minutes instead of half an hour.

The last 50 years of the twentieth century saw influential changes in X-rays and the introduction of entirely new ways of imaging which could also give functional measurements of the tissue or organ being imaged. The introduction of the Seldinger technique made it possible to put catheters into arteries and veins by puncture rather than by cut-down. Angiography therefore flourished and this method later led to steady development in interventional techniques, eg balloon dilatation and stent insertion in arteries. The 1960s saw the development of the use of ultrasound for the investigation of the fetus *in utero*. It was the first diagnostic system not to depend on ionising radiation and this led to its rapid adoption for antenatal diagnosis. It soon began to be used in the examination of abdominal organs such as the kidney, liver and spleen. With increasing sensitivity its use has also spread to other soft parts such as the thyroid and various tendons.

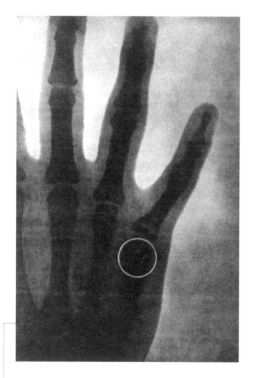

One of the first X-rays taken in London, in 1896, at St Thomas' Hospital. It shows (circled) a fracture in the head and neck of the fifth metacarpal of a medical student's hand. There is no history of how the fracture occurred.

In 1971 the first CT (computerised tomography) scanner was developed. The progress of such scanners since then has come from the work of scientists and engineers, using computers of increasing power. In the 1970s the use of cyclotron-generated radioactive isotopes for diagnosis began to offer information on conditions such as bone metastases, thyroid disorders and pulmonary embolism, and were also used to measure function eg in the kidney. Today the PET (positron emission tomography) scanner employs short-lived isotopes of oxygen or fluorine in the functional evaluation of a range of disorders, particularly malignancy and those affecting the brain. The 1980s saw the introduction of Magnetic Resonance Imaging (MRI) scanners of increasing power and sophistication. MRI scanners do not depend on ionising radiations and can give images in any anatomical plane. Unlike X-rays they can image soft tissues.

It was against the background of these far-reaching developments that the Philip Harris Chair of Radiological Sciences was founded at Guy's and Michael Maisey (b 1939) appointed to this post until his retirement in 2002. His department embraced the new techniques and with a number of physicists on the staff made significant contributions to the analysis of imaging signals, developments in isotope scanning, and image-guided interventions in ENT and neurosurgery.

Under Maisey's leadership the Clinical Pet Centre was established at St Thomas' Hospital in 1992, and was the first clinically-orientated PET centre in the UK. Two new machines recently acquired in 2005 have paired PET with CT scanning, which has enhanced the imaging potential for tumours and also brings new facilities for neuropsychiatric and cardiac investigation and treatment. The department announced a world first in 2002 with its opening of the £3 million Centre for Magnetic Resonance Imaging and Intervention. It was the first centre of its kind in the world to configure magnetic resonance, X-ray and ultrasound in the same room to allow image-guided interventions using all three modalities.

Clinical imaging research today concentrates on novel pairing of different methods of imaging, for example X-ray and MRI. These pairings create powerful combinations to give diagnostic and invasive information significantly greater than either alone, not only in the clinical arena but also for research.

The use of MRI alone to guide the procedure of cardiac catheterization was pioneered at King's. This is usually done using only X-rays to guide the catheter, which has a radio-opaque tip, but the multiple procedures often required in children with congenital heart disease, as well as the less frequent exposures in other patients, have a risk of developing malignancy. The risk is substantial, being 1 in 2,500 for an adult and 1 in 1,000 for a child according to the UK National Radiology Protection Board. MRI,

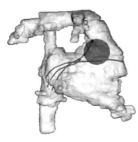

Images from a patient undergoing ablation of an abnormal electrical focus in the heart causing arrhythmias. The location of the ablation catheters is shown by X-ray images which are overlaid on the heart's anatomy derived from MRI (XMR).

as well as reducing this risk, also has the advantage of showing where the catheter is in relation to the chambers, valves and other structures of the heart, which X-rays cannot show.

X-ray + MRI = XMR

The procedure of MRI alone was followed by combining X-rays and MRI in one machine at King's to gain the advantages of both but still reduce X-ray exposure.

The combined approach of XMR has been used for the first time in the world at King's to guide the electrophysiological interventions to treat abnormal rhythms of the heart. Many of these arrhythmias arise from a defined focus in heart, which needs to be mapped by electrodes and then ablated. The combination of X-rays for the metallic electrodes and MRI for the heart chambers allows for very accurate mapping of the abnormal focus. MRI can also record the contractions of the cardiac muscle so that their relationship to the heart's electrical activity recorded simultaneously by the electrodes can be monitored.

PET and MRI – a new partnership

PET is now a mature technology and is being widely used for imaging malignant tumours, neurological lesions and cardiac metabolism. In patients with malignant disease PET can record a tumour's glucose metabolism and levels of internal oxygen which can be superimposed on the surrounding body structures which are defined by MRI. This combination will give detailed information on the response of the tumour to treatment and its effect on surrounding tissues, as well as detailed guidance for biopsies of the tumour.

Many other tracers for the PET examination are now becoming available in addition to the standard one for metabolism. The new tracers can give images of cell proliferation, hypoxia, apoptosis (cell death), angiogenesis (new blood vessel formation in the tumour) and gene expression. These new tools for probing the biology of tumours, treated and untreated, will add greatly to understanding their behaviour and response to treatment.

New techniques applied to MRI are being used at King's to explore new areas and questions in disease and treatment. One example is the adaptation of MRI to examine the microstructure of white matter pathways in the brain in autism spectrum disorder (ASD). This is a neurodevelopmental disorder characterised by impaired social communication and

Glucose metabolism and hypoxia in a large soft tissue sarcoma using the radiotracers 18 FDG (glucose) and 18 FMISO (oxygen). This information from a PET scan is displayed with the anatomical image derived from MRI. The MRI image can be used to guide a biopsy, for example to the part of the tumour with the highest metabolic rate.

repetitive behaviour. It has been suggested that its neurobiological basis includes abnormalities in neural networks of the cerebellum. The cerebellum is one the most highly connected structures of the brain and plays an important role in the development of motor abilities and higher cognitive functions. MRI (*in vivo* diffusion tensor magnetic resonance imaging-based tractography) was used to explore the microstructual integrity of the cerebellar white matter pathways connecting the cerebellum to cerebral cortex ie the brain's higher centres for intellect and behaviour. In ASD there was a significant reduction in microstructural ordering of intra-cerebellar fibres and the main output tract, but normal input tracts. This is the first evidence of localised abnormalities in specific cerebellar circuitry in ASD and adds to its definition as a structural brain disorder.

Imaging stem cells at work

There is virtually no area of medical research that is not affected by discoveries surrounding stem cells, be it their relevance for brain repair, generation of new teeth or even their involvement in depression. Nonetheless, one of the difficulties is to visualise these cells in a living subject. At King's a bimodal imaging method using a novel contrast agent which is visible by both fluorescence and magnetic resonance imaging techniques has been developed. Seamless integration of the agent into stem cells therefore allows their identification *in vivo* (MRI) and subsequent corroboration *ex vivo* by fluorescence microscopy.

This technique has been used to follow the migration of transplanted neural stem cells from their remote site of injection across the brain to the site of a stroke, allowing the study of the dynamic nature of stem cell migration and its influence on functional recovery. Combining stem cell tracking with functional imaging methods (such as functional and pharmacological MRI) will provide an *in vivo* assessment of stem cell differentiation and its contribution to brain plasticity. These interdisciplinary developments using MRI as a core technology will become an integral part of the management of patients undergoing cell therapy.

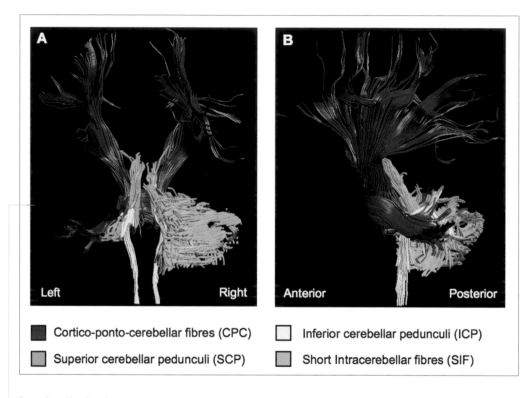

Cortico-ponto-cerebellar fibres (CPC)

Superior cerebellar pedunculi (SCP)

Inferior cerebellar pedunculi (ICP)

Short Intracerebellar fibres (SIF)

Imaging the brain

There are millions of connections between the cells of the brain. Many of these connections are made by groups of nerve fibres (tracts) connecting one part of the brain to another. If the tracts are disrupted, wrongly connected, or their number of nerve fibres reduced, then the function(s) served by those tracts will be impaired. Viewing these connecting tracts *in vivo* has been made possible by a new technique using MRI - tractography - which gives anatomical information available previously only at postmortem. The image is of a normal cerebellum using tractography to show its white matter connections. The green tracts are the major cerebellar output, connecting to the contralateral cerebral hemisphere (Panel A is a coronal posterior view and panel B is a sagittal left view).

Robert McCance FRS
(1898-1993)

Elsie Widdowson CBE FRS
(1906-2000)

John Yudkin (1910-1995)

Arnold Bender (1918-1999)

Gerald Russell (b 1928)

We are what we eat: the science of nutrition

King's has played a key part in establishing nutrition as an academic subject and encouraging public interest and awareness in the food we eat and its effect on our health. The College's longstanding roles in research and in training nutritionists and dieticians also extend into the study of eating disorders at the Institute of Psychiatry.

A healthy partnership

The famous team of McCance and Widdowson, authors of the nutritionists' bible, *The Chemical Composition of Foods*, was formed in the kitchens of King's College Hospital in 1933 when Dr Elsie Widdowson (1906-2000), a postgraduate student of dietetics at King's, met Dr Robert McCance (1898-1993), a clinical scientist and head of the Hospital's biochemical laboratory. The scientific partnership was consolidated when in 1938 McCance became reader in medicine at Cambridge and Widdowson joined him there. They realized that to study the effects of diet on physiology it was essential to have detailed knowledge of the nutrient composition of food. In 1940 the first edition of *The Chemical Composition of Foods* was published as a Medical Research Council special report. It became a factual basis for innumerable nutritional studies throughout the world

as it documented the nutritional content of thousands of foods. During their 60 year partnership McCance and Widdowson also studied the effects of rationing during the Second World War, the effects of diet on infant growth and development, and nutritional principles such as the relation between disease risk and nutrient intakes and the effect of early nutrition on health later in life.

Nutrition as an academic discipline

John Yudkin, Professor of Nutrition at Queen Elizabeth College (QEC) from 1954 to 1971, was not only the UK's first professor of the subject but an international pioneer of the science of nutrition and a household name from the 1960s to the 1980s. He was also the author of *The Slimmer's Cookbook* (1961, written with Gweneth Chappell, a senior lecturer in food science at QEC) which was the first popular slimming

book with a solid scientific basis which took social factors into account in an intelligent way.

In the 1950s Yudkin challenged the hypothesis that the high incidence of coronary heart disease in the West was due to fat in the diet. In *The Lancet* in 1957 he demolished the existing incriminatory evidence against fat, proposing that heart disease was instead 'at least partly attributable to the misbalance of energy expenditure in a society where people were eating too much and exercising too little'. In *This Slimming Business* (1958), the first of his very popular books, he argued (in terms familiar to followers of the Atkins Diet) that the correct way to diet was to cut out the least nutritious elements – carbohydrates – while continuing to eat protein and fat.

In the 1960s he claimed that it was a high intake of sugar, rather than fat, which caused heart disease, and in 1972 his all-out attack on sugar, in *Pure, White and Deadly*, linked sugar with a whole range of other illnesses including diabetes and arthritis, and paid particular attention to its ill effects on children. Yudkin's advocacy of meat and dairy products became increasingly contrary to the prevailing nutritional wisdom, and he was attacked by the powerful sugar lobby for accepting funding from the dairy industry. Yudkin was, nevertheless, always scrupulous about the advice he gave the public: 'Some of the things I have told you are important facts; some are less important opinions of my own'.

Frederick Gowland Hopkins

A Nobel recognition for vitamins

Sir Frederick Gowland Hopkins (1861–1947) graduated in chemistry at University College London and later studied medicine at Guy's. After qualifying in 1894 he lectured there on physiology and toxicology. He moved to Cambridge in 1898 to develop biochemistry, and was appointed to the university's chair in this new discipline in 1914. He was awarded the Nobel Prize for Physiology or Medicine in 1929 with Christiaan Eijkman for the discovery of vitamins, which Hopkins had shown were 'accessory substances' essential for the normal growth of rats.

Arnold Bender (1918-1999) was appointed as Senior Lecturer at QEC by Yudkin in 1965, having previously worked in industry as well as in academia, and he went on to become Professor of Nutrition and Dietetics at QEC between 1971 and 1983. He made important links between food science and nutrition and developed with Derek Miller (also later appointed to QEC) the oft-cited Bender-Miller Net Protein Utilisation method of assaying the nutritive value of proteins.

Broad approach

The Department of Nutrition and Dietetics became part of King's College London on the merger between QEC and King's in 1985. The work undertaken in the department continues to reflect the broad approach to the science of nutrition, defined as understanding the effects of food on the body in health and disease. Research falls into three main areas: public health, the molecular basis of nutrition and eating disorders.

Nutrition and the population

Nutrition is recognized to be of immense importance to public health, as poor nutrition and obesity are major causes of heart disease, diabetes and cancer.

Large scale projects at King's are evaluating the effects of changing the amounts of and types of fats and carbohydrates on insulin resistance and the risk of cardiovascular disease, and the effect of increasing fruit and vegetable intake on vascular function.

Iron: too much and too little

Lack of iron leads to the only common nutritional deficiency in the UK – iron deficiency anaemia – whereas excess iron absorption and storage in the body leads to the uncommon disease haemochromatosis which can prove fatal by iron deposits in heart or liver. Genes and their products have been identified in the duodenum which affect iron absorption and are regulated by iron levels, and so should lead to ways to alter absorption appropriately to treat these disorders.

New knowledge of iron metabolism also opens a new way of treating bacterial infection. Invading bacteria need iron, so using their surface receptors they scavenge the host's iron stores. Defining the receptors and their site of action on the protein-bound iron in the host will allow the development of drugs to block these mechanisms and so deny iron to the bacteria and counter the infection.

Sucralose: a sweet success

In 1976, a research team at Queen Elizabeth College was examining the chemistry of sucrose, supported by Tate & Lyle. Contrary to previous knowledge, they discovered that certain derivatives of sucrose are very much sweeter than sucrose itself. The discovery is attributed to a fortuitous misunderstanding. A graduate student, Shashikant Phadnis, misinterpreted the instruction to 'test' the chlorinated sucrose derivatives, and 'tasted' them instead, resulting in the surprising discovery that they can be up to 600 times sweeter than sucrose itself. Sucralose is approximately twice as sweet as saccharin and four times as sweet as aspartame and, unlike aspartame, it is heat stable over a broad range of pH, making it amenable to use in baking and in products that require a longer shelf life. Sucralose has now been approved for use in over 80 countries. It was marketed for table-top use and as an ingredient direct to manufacturers, and 30 years after the original discovery, over 4,000 products now use sucralose.

Eating disorders

The eating disorders anorexia nervosa, bulimia and binge-purge anorexia nervosa are often in the public eye because of their increasing frequency. Eating disorders predominate in young women and affect eight to ten per cent of women.

Anorexia nervosa is not a modern disease. The first description came from Guy's physician Sir William Gull (1816-1890). The mortality rate of patients with eating disorders can be as high as 25 per cent in anorexia nervosa. Understanding what causes eating disorders is the aim of the Eating Disorders Unit at the Institute of Psychiatry.

The Unit was established in 1979 by Professor Gerald Russell (b 1928), in the same year that he gave the first modern description of bulimia nervosa, categorising it as 'an ominous variant of anorexia nervosa'.

In 2003 researchers at the Unit were among an international team which identified two genes on chromosome 1 which confer half the risk for developing eating disorders, and they act on brain receptors for serotonin. This finding links with abnormal MRI brain scans in those with eating disorders. The Unit's studies have shown that patients shown food have increased brain activity in an area of the frontal lobes which normally governs the individual's basic behaviour and which is also associated with obsessive/compulsive disorders and drug addiction. In bulimia patients, food stimuli reduce activity in a frontal lobe area which normally inhibits behavioural responses. If these abnormal brain responses to food could be modified by training, food itself or drugs, then an interesting avenue of treatment would be opened.

The Unit is also involved in Europe-wide studies to evaluate environmental risk factors for eating disorders. It is thought that events before and after a child's birth as well as cultural attitudes towards food and diet are key triggers for the development of eating disorders. The studies will examine national differences and also sister pairs, where one of the two has an eating disorder, to define individual differences. The study is also an opportunity to study male patients with eating disorders, who account for ten per cent of sufferers.

Eating disorders affect eight to ten per cent of young women. Images of food are used at the Institute of Psychiatry to pinpoint brain activity in people suffering from anorexia.

Sir John Simon FRS
(1816-1904)

Walter Holland CBE
(b 1929)

A *healthier population: advancements in public health*

In Victorian Britain, living in the city came with serious health risks. Life expectancy for those living in the cities in the 1850s, with high rates of cholera, typhoid and smallpox, was as little as 26 compared with 57 for those who lived in the country.

While the first interest at King's in community health came from Thomas Hodgkin (1798-1866) who lectured lay audiences on the importance of proper sewage disposal and the dangers of excess alcohol, smoking and occupational dust exposure, some of the most significant advancements in public health in the nineteenth century in England were led by John Simon (1816-1904). Although recognised for his knowledge of science as an anatomy demonstrator and pathologist, as well as his skills as surgeon, he was to save more lives with his pen than his scalpel.

In 1848 he was appointed the first Medical Officer of Health to the City of London, and only the second in the country. Then, London, like all big cities, was rife with infectious diseases, many, largely cholera, borne by widespread untreated sewage and a lack of clean water supply.

In this appointment and his later position as Chief Medical Officer of Health to the General Board of Health in 1855, he put sanitation in the spotlight and

afforded a secure basis for future legislation. Simon exposed the appalling health conditions in the city and initiated studies into the causes of disease. He urged reform in water supply, sewerage, drainage, burial practices, urban overcrowding and a vaccination programme for smallpox. With statistical evidence and his medical knowledge he was able to show that lives could be saved by good sanitation.

One of Simon's greatest achievements was that sanitation and its impact on public health came under the direct supervision of the medical department, and was not just a matter for engineers, and that prevention of disease should be regarded as the highest motive for official action. Furthermore, his work was influential in the development of public health legislation; most notably the Sanitary Act 1866, Public Health Act 1875 and the Vaccination Act 1881.

Through all this time Simon continued at St Thomas' both as surgeon and lecturer in pathology. In his lectures, he continued to promulgate the latest

Contaminated water was largely responsible for outbreaks of disease including cholera in Victorian Britain.

Cartoon portrayal of John Simon in his role as the first Medical Officer of Health for the City of London putting pressure on the Corporation of London to act upon the pestilential conditions of the graveyards in the City.

scientific findings and their relevance to medical practice. Although his role in the hospital continued to be surgeon and pathologist, in 1856 he arranged for the appointment of the first lecturer in public health in England outside the military, so founding public health as an academic discipline.

Academic department of public health

The appointment of Walter Holland (b 1929) at St Thomas' in 1962 was the first academic post (later chair) in public health with an honorary consultant contract recognising the vital interplay between public health and clinical medicine. The importance of his work was soon recognized by the Department of Health which funded its first independent research unit at St Thomas'. A number of studies, influential in shaping Government health policy followed under Holland's leadership.

Studies of children

In studies of children in the 1960s, the department showed that passive smoking in babies and active smoking in young children increased respiratory infections and reduced long-term ventilatory function. This work was highly influential in leading the government to warn parents and pregnant women of these effects. The department's Nutritional Intake Study in the 1970s surprisingly demonstrated that removing free school meals and free milk did not alter total nutritional intake and contributed to the Government's decision to withdraw the scheme.

Hospital and community practice

The department made several important contributions to hospital and community practice. Following World War II damage, the planned rebuilding at St Thomas' in the 1960s raised the question of what sort of

facilities should be provided. The first UK questionnaire to examine the incidence of disability in the local population showed gross deficiencies in the care of these patients, but not those with acute medical conditions needing admission, outpatient treatment, or diagnostic services. This was the first time that such information was made available to influence new hospital build. An increasing concern around this time was the appropriate hospital stay. A random controlled trial of two-day stay versus seven-ten day showed no effect medically and no difference in social cost as time off work was the same; no savings to the NHS would result unless beds were closed. These findings had a major impact on hospital practice in the UK.

Whether to screen for disease is a common medico-political controversy. In the 1970s a trial of multiphasic screening (for several factors in each individual such as blood pressure, vision, hearing, lung function tests etc) was carried out in several GP practices in St Paul's Cray on the outskirts of London. The measured outcomes were death, morbidity, time off work, need for home-help, use of GP and hospital admission. All were unchanged by screening; this result had a profound impact on government policy at the time.

'Avoidable mortality' became an important concept to examine medical practice and provision of facilities; it rested on the assumption that illnesses such as acute respiratory infection and acute appendicitis should have low death rates. A survey of death rates for twelve similar conditions in England surprisingly found a six-fold variation in mortality but not related to social deprivation, giving rise to changes in the provision of services. Observations based on this study have now been extended to Europe.

General practitioners are changing the delivery of health care by the increasing development in their practices of special interests including paediatrics, cardiology, dermatology, orthopaedics and ophthalmology. Moving a part of these specialties from hospital practice will have important effects which are being evaluated at King's.

Common disorders

Research at King's today continues to focus on common community disorders in South London. Many such as diabetes, hypertension and stroke are over-represented owing to social deprivation and a high proportion of ethnic minorities. The South London Stroke Register studies the epidemiology of stroke and delivery of health care. It is also part of the European Register of Strokes which examines variation in the acute management of strokes and reasons for its unequal outcome across different countries.

A surprisingly large proportion of prescribed drugs are not taken by patients. A review of concordance - the degree to which a prescribed treatment is followed - found that some but not all of the essential information is given to patients, and that they are not sufficiently involved in discussing or choosing their medication.

John Haighton FRS
(1755-1823)

James Blundell
(1790-1878)

John Lever (1811-1859)

John Braxton Hicks
(1823-1897)

Pregnancy & childbirth: reducing the hazards

Complications and death in childbirth were expected risks for women before the twentieth century, most notably from eclampsia, sepsis and haemorrhage.

While deaths from all other causes fell from about 1890, rates of maternal mortality in Britain did not improve until the 1940s. Significant reductions in the immediate risks of childbirth can be attributed to the advancement of blood transfusion, which began in the nineteenth century with the investigations of Guy's obstetrician James Blundell (1790-1878).

While maternal mortality has been greatly reduced, pregnancy is still inseparable from potential hazards for the child and the mother. The Maternal & Fetal Research Unit at King's continues research into prevention of pre-eclampsia, a potentially fatal condition. The Unit is complementing this research with other long-term studies suggesting how improvements in the health of pregnant women can help to secure lifelong health for their children.

James Blundell: pioneer of transfusion

Obstetrics was a family concern for James Blundell. Following medical training at Guy's and St Thomas' and also at Edinburgh he worked as a lecturer with his uncle John Haighton (1755-1823) at Guy's. Together

they gave some of the largest classes of midwifery in London. Haighton himself was a noted physiologist who developed instruments for the delivery of babies including early designs of forceps. In 1818 upon his uncle's death he succeeded him to the chair of physiology and obstetrics at the combined schools of St Thomas' and Guy's Hospitals. Blundell's lectures attracted the largest numbers in London. In 1821 he carried out a series of experiments on animals from which he proposed bolder abdominal surgery. He performed the removal of a cancerous uterus vaginally which was the first operation of its kind in Britain. It was during this time that Blundell became interested in the operation of the transfusion of blood.

In the nineteenth century mortality of pregnant women was one in 100. As an obstetrician, Blundell witnessed many women dying from post-partum haemorrhage. At this time blood-letting was still regarded as a useful treatment for haemorrhage, while transfusion had been banned from medical practice since 1667. Blundell thought that death by haemorrhage could be prevented by revisiting the idea of transfusing blood.

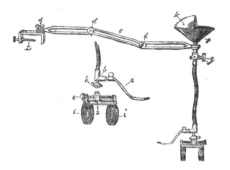

He initiated a series of experiments performed on dogs which constitute one of the first systematic and extensive experiments upon transfusion of blood. Blundell argued that transfusions should be used solely to replace lost blood (and not to treat mental disorders as was earlier the case) and was the first to suggest that only human blood should be given to humans. Blundell devised a series of instruments for the perfection of the transfusion of human to human blood including the 'Impeller'.

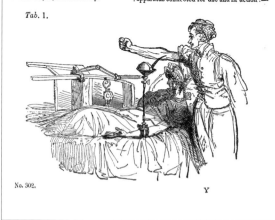

THE LANCET.

Vol. II.]　　　LONDON, SATURDAY, JUNE 13.　　　[1828-9.

OBSERVATIONS

ON

TRANSFUSION OF BLOOD.

By Dr. BLUNDELL.

*With a Description of his Gravitator.**

STATES of the body really requiring the infusion of blood into the veins are probably rare; yet we sometimes meet with cases in which the patient must die unless such operation can be performed; and still more frequently with cases which seem to require a supply of blood, in order to prevent the ill health which usually arises from large losses of the vital fluid, even when they do not prove fatal.

＊ The instrument is manufactured by Messrs. Maw, 55, Aldermanbury.

In the present state of our knowledge respecting the operation, although it has not been clearly shown to have proved fatal in any one instance, yet not to mention possible, though unknown risks, inflammation of the arm has certainly been produced by it on one or two occasions; and therefore it seems right, as the operation now stands, to confine transfusion to the first class of cases only, namely, those in which there seems to be no hope for the patient, unless blood can be thrown into the veins.

The object of the Gravitator is, to give help in this last extremity, by transmitting the blood in a regulated stream from one individual to another, with as little exposure as may be to air, cold, and inanimate surface; ordinary venesection being the only operation performed on the person who emits the blood; and the insertion of a small tube into the vein usually laid open in bleeding, being all the operation which it is necessary to execute on the person who receives it.

The following plate represents the whole apparatus connected for use and in action:—

Tab. 1.

No. 302.　　　　　　　　　　　　　Y

The instrument was attached to a chair (pictured far left). A vein in the patient's arm was then incised and the tubule introduced and held in place by an assistant. The blood donor would sit in the chair, their arm opened by a lancet and blood directed into a cup attached. The blood would then be impelled into the vein of the patient. Blundell was aware that any delay in transmitting the blood from the donor risked clotting. In 1828, he published 'Observations on Transfusion of Blood' (left) in *The Lancet* with a description of his transfusion 'Gravitator', a funnel and syringe system designed to prevent coagulation.

Over the course of five years, Blundell performed ten documented human to human blood transfusions, with five patients recovering as a result – more than any other man before him. Having no knowledge of blood groups, Blundell's success rate was limited but his investigations revived the study of blood transfusion after 150 years of neglect. Not only did he establish that only human blood can be used in transfusion, he made observations which were to enable the future development of blood transfusion and give him his reputation as the 'father of the operation of the transfusion'.

In 1843 John Lever **right** published a paper on a series of cases of convulsions in pregnancy, observing swelling of the ankles, puffiness around the eyelids, and albumin in the urine. Lever's work led to the belief that eclampsia was a renal disease, a form of nephritis.

Preparing for labour

In 1872 Guy's obstetrician, John Braxton Hicks (1823-1897), was the first physician to describe podalic version of the fetus and the contractions of the uterus which are known by his name. These are normally painless contractions, which do not lead to childbirth, and begin as early as the third month of pregnancy. Braxton Hicks also played a role in developing James Blundell's techniques of human blood transfusion. He was the first to use phosphate of soda mixed with the donor blood to prevent coagulation.

Tommy's the Baby Charity Maternal & Fetal Research Unit was established in 1995 at King's. Its major research focus is early detection and also prevention of pre-eclampsia and pre-term labour, and the effects of maternal health on the life term health of babies.

Pre-eclampsia

Pre-eclampsia today remains one of the commonest complications of pregnancy, affecting four per cent of pregnant women. The only cure is delivery which, if premature, brings with it risks for the baby. Pre-eclampsia is responsible for the death of 600 babies and seven mothers in the UK each year.

John Lever (1811-1859) of Guy's Hospital was the first to describe the presence of protein in the urine, which is a crucial indication, with high blood pressure, that a pregnant woman is at risk of eclampsia. Pre-eclampsia was later distinguished from eclampsia in 1910 when blood pressure measurements began.

John Haighton's forceps.

Instruments of the trade

John Haighton was a prolific obstetric operator and developed some of the earliest instruments for delivering babies including forceps. By the early eighteenth century the use of forceps by physicians was widespread throughout Europe. Obstetricians began to refine the design as they saw fit.

In skilled hands these instruments aided the positive outcome of many obstructed labours.

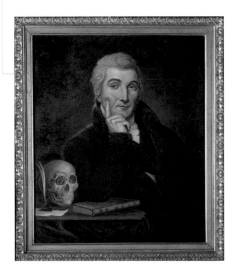

Contributions to biomedicine *a continuing story*

A pilot study has shown that when women at risk of pre-eclampsia are given vitamins C and E, the risk is reduced by 50 per cent.

Supplementary evidence

Initial studies at King's conducted by the Maternal & Fetal Research Unit showed that when women at risk of pre-eclampsia were given vitamin C and E supplements, the risk of the disease was halved, presumably by removal of free radicals.

The Unit has recently conducted a study of 2,400 pregnant women with known clinical risk factors for pre-eclampsia, drawn from 22 hospitals across the UK, in a large-scale placebo-controlled trial of the effect of vitamins C and E in pregnancy. This trial is being complemented by a worldwide study in collaboration with the World Health Organisation. If the preventative approach can be proven, the impact on maternal mortality rates will be huge, particularly in the developing world. Today, 90 per cent of maternal deaths occur in the developing world, where pregnancy is the major cause of mortality in women of child-bearing age.

Detecting pre-eclampsia

The Unit is concerned with the accurate measurement of blood pressure. It has considerable research strength in developing and testing devices for accurate measurement of blood pressure in pregnancy and eclampsia and developing new algorithms and techniques in direct blood pressure assessment.

While mercury manometers are being phased out and replaced by automated devices there are concerns about their limited accuracy in some clinically important situations: exercise, pregnancy and critical illness. The research group, together with colleagues in the Cardiovascular Division, has developed a new method for the measurement of blood pressure based on the combination of a standard cuff and a non-invasive peripheral arterial pressure sensor, and is evaluating this device.

King's offers the only national blood pressure validation service for the assessment of blood pressure devices. The Unit recently validated the Microlife pregnancy monitor as an accurate device for the pre-eclamptic population. The Microlife pregnancy monitor, which is now being marketed in the UK, allows mothers to accurately record daily their own blood pressure, enabling pre-eclampsia to be diagnosed earlier in pregnancy.

Researchers have assessed the accuracy of blood pressure monitors used in primary care, finding that one in five had significant calibration drift, with implications for the treatment of hundreds of thousands of patients – whether it is inappropriate treatment through overestimation or missed diagnosis through underestimation. A national calibration testing strategy is now being prepared.

Fetal origins of adult disease

There is increasing evidence that maternal nutritional status may permanently programme the fetus to develop cardiovascular disease and diabetes in later life. The developmental origins of adult disease is a rapidly expanding area of research at King's, and interest in maternal health has recently extended to a study of nutrition in teenage pregnancy and its effect on the long-term health of the child, particularly in relation to cardiovascular disease and diabetes.

Other current research in the Unit includes assessment of maternal care, access and inequity. With the hope that the immediate dangers of pregnancy are at last receding, researchers are now able to take a long-term view of pregnancy as the starting point for lifelong health.

James Blundell (1790-1878) · Sir George Frederic Still (1868-1941) · Ronald MacKeith (1908-1977) · Paul Polani FRS (1914-2006) · Jon Scopes (1920-1999) · Sir Eric Stroud (1924-2005) · Alex Mowat (1935-1995) · Sir Cyril Chantler (b 1939)

Growth of paediatrics & child health

Until the twentieth century paediatrics was regarded as something of a medical backwater. King's Professor Sir George Frederic Still played a major part in changing that perception and was a key figure in establishing paediatrics as a clinical specialty.

King's alumna Dr Cicely Delphine Williams, Professor Paul Polani and Dr Ronald MacKeith were among those who advanced the discipline, and many Guy's, King's and St Thomas' paediatricians continue to make contributions to this area, particularly through the rebuilt Evelina Children's Hospital – London's first new children's hospital for a hundred years.

Before the mid-eighteenth century, care and treatment of sick children were not separated from the treatment of adults and paediatrics had to wait until the end of the nineteenth century to be formally recognised as a clinical specialty.

Specialist 'lying-in' hospitals emerged in the mid-eighteenth century. They were hospitals for pregnant women and newborn babies who were not admitted to general hospitals. The medical students and staff of the teaching hospitals did, however, help to deliver children at home. Among the early 'accoucheurs' was James Blundell (1790-1878), Professor of Obstetrics at

Guy's, who was the first to use intratracheal intubation to resuscitate newborn babies in 1834 (see also pages 51-52).

Child mortality was very high – and higher in London than elsewhere – mainly owing to whooping cough, tuberculosis, pneumonia, diphtheria, scarlet fever and measles. There was nonetheless opposition to the idea of hospitals specifically for children because of fears that they might spread infectious diseases. Florence Nightingale suggested that, rather than creating separate children's hospitals or wards, it was better to place children among adults: 'The woman in the next bed… often becomes the child's best protector and nurse. And it does her as much good as it does the child,' she wrote in 1863.

Birth of hospitals for children

Despite widespread opposition to a hospital dedicated to care for sick children, Great Ormond Hospital for

The Prince and Princess of Wales visit the Evelina Hospital for Sick Children, 1890. The hospital was originally located in Southwark Bridge Road and relocated to Guy's in 1975. It remained there for 20 years before it was rebuilt at St Thomas' Hospital, reopening in 2005.

Children, opened in 1852, was first located in a house previously owned by St Thomas' physician Richard Mead. It was the first hospital for children in the English-speaking world.

The Evelina Hospital for Sick Children opened in 1869 in Southwark. Founded by Baron Ferdinand de Rothschild, its name commemorated his wife Evelina who had died in childbirth in 1866. The Evelina was intended to provide Southwark with the most up-to-date child care facilities. The hospital included a flexible layout to allow for playrooms and the need to quarantine infectious children. The Evelina transferred to Guy's Hospital in 1975 and was rebuilt in 2005 at St Thomas' Hospital.

A new kind of children's hospital

In 2005 the Evelina Children's Hospital moved into a new £60 million building at St Thomas' Hospital. It is London's first new children's hospital for more than 100 years and is the result of intensive consultations with patients and their families. The seven-storey, glass-fronted building houses not only 140 beds but also a gallery, performance space, café, hospital school, bright red rocket lifts and a 17-foot high helter-skelter. Its design is expected to influence the building of new hospitals in Britain and across the world. Special accommodation for staff from the King's College London School of Medicine will ensure that interaction between clinical and research teams is maximised.

George Frederic Still, Britain's first professor of diseases of children.

First professor of childhood diseases

George Frederic Still (1868-1941) has been described as the father of British clinical paediatrics for his part in establishing child health as a separate field of clinical study and practice.

Following graduation from Cambridge he undertook medical training at Guy's Hospital qualifying in 1894. He demonstrated his scientific interest in childhood diseases early in his career. At the age of only 29 he described a rare type of rheumatoid arthritis in children, known as Still's disease, in his MD thesis 'A special form of joint disease met with in children'. He is one of a few distinguished by having an eponym named after an MD thesis. From appointments at Great Ormond Street Hospital, he joined King's in 1899 as Physician for Diseases of Children at King's College London, making King's (then still in central London) the first teaching hospital to establish a paediatric department.

In 1906 Still was promoted at King's to become Britain's first professor of diseases of children, and his book *Common Diseases of Children*, published in 1909, became one of the most popular paediatric texts of its day achieving five editions.

Still became the first chair of the first national group of paediatricians in 1928 known as the British Paediatric Association. The aim of the association was the advancement of the study of paediatrics and the promotion of friendship amongst paediatricians. This became the Royal College of Paediatricians and Child

Boy of eight with Still's disease. The disease was first described by George Frederic Still, Britain's first professor of diseases of children.

Health in 1996 and now has some 6,000 members and is the training body for the paediatricians in the UK.

In 1934 Still became an emeritus professor at King's. In 1937 he was knighted for having been the personal physician to princesses Elisabeth and Margaret and was also appointed KCVO in recognition of his devotion to the welfare of children.

Paediatrics in the twentieth century

The development of children's hospitals and paediatric departments within general hospitals produced the essential concentration of patients and expertise to stimulate research. Later and inevitably, as in adult medicine and surgery, subspecialties grew in paediatrics strengthening the impetus to research and greater clinical expertise. This pattern was seen at Guy's, King's College and St Thomas' Hospitals during the 1960s-70s. Among the first were paediatric cardiology and intensive care led by Michael Joseph and the introduction by Ronald MacKeith (1908-1977) of developmental child neurology in the UK. MacKeith set up a pioneering clinic for children with cerebral palsy which allowed various specialists (paediatric neurologists, orthopaedic surgeons, ophthalmologists and audiologists) to meet together and consult with the children and their families. This model was replicated around the country. MacKeith was concerned not only with movement disability but also with the whole range of chronic neurological disability in childhood, including vision and hearing difficulties,

Cicely Williams – pioneering child nutritionist and campaigner

After graduating from Oxford University in 1920 Cicely Delphine Williams (1893-1992) undertook clinical training at King's College Hospital including the study of paediatrics with Sir George Frederic Still. Dr Williams was born in Jamaica, where she noticed debilitating and often fatal symptoms affecting young children, and whilst working with the British Colonial Service in the Gold Coast (now Ghana) she identified the protein deficiency disease 'kwashiorkor', a word from the Ga language meaning 'disease of the deposed child', because this syndrome afflicts children who have been abruptly banished from the maternal breast by the arrival of a new baby. In Singapore in 1939 she gave a lecture entitled 'Milk and Murder', condemning companies which promoted sales of tinned milk and led mothers to give up breastfeeding.

While imprisoned by the Japanese in Changi Gaol during World War II she was able to use her knowledge of protein deficiency to treat her fellow prisoners and keep the death rate lower than in other camps. Williams continued to be active in the debate over protein nutrition throughout her life. She was equally important as a pioneer of maternal and child care in developing countries with a system based on local traditions and resources rather than on the use of expensive drugs and western systems of child care: a philosophy she expounded as first Head of the Maternal and Child Health Section of the World Health Organisation from 1948 to 1951. She was the first woman to be elected to an honorary fellowship of the Royal College of Medicine, in 1977.

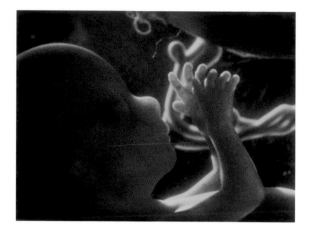

King's researchers and clinicians have pioneered advanced techniques for surgery in the womb. Fetal diaphragmatic hernia can now be corrected from the 15th week of pregnancy. King's researchers have also identified key factors in fetal development which can be used to more easily detect abnormalities including Down's syndrome. Researchers have associated the absence of nasal bone with around 70-75 per cent of Down's syndrome babies.

language problems, epilepsy and complex behaviour problems. MacKeith also championed open access for parents to their children in hospital, to reduce the devastating psychological outcomes often following long term admissions.

Liver and renal paediatric units began at King's and Guy's under the leadership of Alex Mowat (1935-1995) and Cyril Chantler respectively (b 1939) (see chapter 19). Taking note of the local high incidence of sickle cell disease, Eric Stroud (1924-2005), instigated a clinical service for afflicted children. Two specialties peculiar to paediatrics are neonatal intensive care, developed at St Thomas by Harold Gamsu and Jon Scopes (1920-1995), and fetal medicine at King's College Hospital. Genetics plays a particular role in paediatrics and was established as a specialty in 1960 with Paul Polani (1914-2006) as its director and the UK's first professor of paediatric research (see page 28).

Fetal medicine

Among the most revolutionary advances in medicine over the last twenty years has been the application to the fetus *in utero* of ultrasound for imaging and operative techniques, biopsy samples and correcting congenital defects. The Harris Birthright Research Centre at King's College Hospital has been at the forefront of fetal medicine since it was established in 1984. It has an international reputation for development and the validation of antenatal diagnostic tests which have transformed obstetric practice by increasing the range and accuracy of diagnosis of congenital defects. The Centre has also been a leader in devising new operative techniques to take fetal samples and correct congenital abnormalities *in utero*. It remains one of the largest fetal medicine research centres in the world and sees 2,000 patients annually.

Diagnosis of Down's in utero

The Centre has been responsible for discovering a crucial ultrasound diagnostic abnormality – an increase of fluid in the neck (increased nuchal transparency thickness) which can be used to detect more than 50 congenital abnormalities, including Down's syndrome. Approximately 1 in a 1,000 babies are born with Down's syndrome so screening for this condition is a high priority for pregnant women.

In 2001 the Centre linked the absence of nasal bone as being associated with 70-75 per cent of babies with Down's syndrome (compared with 1 per cent without). Combining this test with that for the abnormality in the neck and already available blood tests has improved the detection rate for Down's syndrome to around 90 per cent of cases.

The advantage of detecting Down's syndrome and other congenital abnormalities by these non-invasive methods is that it does away with the need for invasive procedures on the fetus. As these carry a significant risk of fetal loss, the potential loss of normal healthy babies is avoided.

Another method of fetal assessment *in utero* is blood flow measurements by the Doppler technique, which provide effective screening for pre-eclampsia and fetal retardation.

Surgery in the womb

The Centre has pioneered several intrauterine procedures to correct deficiencies or correct congenital defects. Among these are transfusions of blood or platelets, and inserting a shunt between the pleural cavity and the amniotic fluid to drain pleural effusions. At a more complex level in 2004 the Centre devised a treatment for congenital diaphragmatic hernia, which impairs lung growth, by inserting a balloon in the fetal trachea from the 15th to the 23rd weeks of pregnancy.

Henry Maudsley
(1835-1918)

Sir Aubrey Lewis
(1900-1975)

Eliot Slater (1904-1983)

Sir Michael Rutter CBE FRS
(b 1933)

Sir David Goldberg
(b 1934)

Health in mind: psychiatry & psychiatric research

The Institute of Psychiatry (IoP), which became a School of King's College London in 1997, is closely linked with the South London and Maudsley NHS Trust, including the famous Bethlem Royal Hospital. The Institute is a leading centre for teaching and research and hosts two Medical Research Council centres.

Bethlem

The Bethlem Royal Hospital was founded in 1247 by Simon Fitzmary as a priory dedicated to St Mary of Bethlehem. Its site in Bishopsgate in the City of London now lies under Liverpool Street Station. The first definite evidence of its use to house mentally ill patients dates from 1403, making Bethlem probably the oldest mental hospital in the world. In 1676 Bethlem moved to a grand and famous building in Moorfields designed by Robert Hooke. The term 'bedlam', derived from the Hospital's name and used to indicate a scene of turmoil or confusion, reflects the way in which Bethlem was open to the public. It became notorious because of the sightseers who thronged its galleries, until indiscriminate public visiting was ended in 1770. In 1815 the Hospital moved to St George's Fields, Southwark, and some of its former buildings are now occupied by the Imperial

War Museum. In 1930 the hospital relocated again to Monks Orchard, Beckenham, south of London. The Maudsley Hospital was founded by Dr Henry Maudsley (1835-1918) and opened in 1923: in 1948 it and Bethlem merged, and since 1999 both hospitals have been part of the South London and Maudsley NHS Trust.

Birth of academic psychiatry

In 1948 the Maudsley's medical school gained independent status within the University of London as the Institute of Psychiatry (IoP). Its first director was Professor (later Sir) Aubrey Lewis (1900-1975), who played a key role in establishing psychiatry as an academic discipline. Almost all of the first generation of professors of psychiatry in the UK derived from the Maudsley and owed much of their approach to research to what they had learned from him. More

The seal and character of Simon Fitzmary as it appears on the Bethlem Foundation deed. The seal depicts Virgin and child, emphasising Fitzmary's 'special devotion' to the Virgin Mary which prompted him to found a priory in her honour.

The founder of the Maudsley Hospital, Dr Henry Maudsley: an eminent psychiatrist who gave £30,000 to the London County Council to found a hospital within three or four miles of Trafalgar Square.

The final scene of William Hogarth's *The Rake's Progress* (1735) where the Rake is dying in 'Bedlam'. At this stage visitors were freely allowed to inspect the patients, and two fashionable ladies can be seen in the role of sightseers.

than any other individual Lewis was responsible for making psychiatry respected within the universities and the field of medicine as a whole. He had a notably broad vision of what were needed as the basic sciences underlying psychiatry, and most of the departments of the Institute of Psychiatry initially grew out of his own department of psychiatry there. He also established social psychiatry as a field of enquiry, and the MRC Social Psychiatry Research Unit that he directed was primarily responsible for making Britain the world leader in this field.

Professor Sir Michael Rutter, founder of the MRC Child Psychiatry Unit and the MRC Social, Genetic and Developmental Psychiatry Centre, who established child psychiatry as an academic, as well as a clinical, discipline.

Twins Jemma and Jennifer Abdul Malique Bello with HRH The Princess Royal at the opening of the Social, Genetic and Developmental Psychiatry Building in February 2003.

Sir David Goldberg, after whom the David Goldberg Centre for Mental Health Services at the Institute of Psychiatry is named.

Nature & nurture

Eliot Slater (1904-1983) was the founder and Director of the Psychiatric Genetics Unit at the IoP (opened in 1959). In 1936 Slater established the Maudsley Hospital Twin Register, thus founding a system which made possible a whole range of psychiatric genetic studies. The Twins' Early Development Study (TEDS), established in the 1990s, uses the same concept as the Maudsley Hospital twin register but is based on a national sample of twins in the general population, rather than just on those attending clinics. TEDS tracks the development of 15,000 pairs of twins born in England and Wales between 1994 and 1996. New research, based on studies of over 3,600 seven-year-old twins, has suggested that early-onset antisocial behaviour in children with psychopathic tendencies is largely inherited.

Possibly the most famous, though highly controversial, name in post-war British psychology, Hans Eysenck, was Professor of Psychology at the IoP from 1955 to 1983. Eysenck was a major contributor to the modern scientific theory of personality, a brilliant teacher who also played a crucial role in the establishment of behavioural treatments for mental disorders. There have, however, been ethical concerns about his approach to race and intelligence, and questions have been raised about the validity of some of his claims on other topics. As a result, he brought some embarrassment to the IoP, as well as fame and credit.

Professor Sir Michael Rutter (b 1933), founder (in 1984) and Director of the MRC Child Psychiatry Unit at the IoP, and subsequently founder and Director of the MRC Social, Genetic and Developmental Psychiatry Centre (1994-8), established child psychiatry as an academic, as well as a clinical, discipline. His research was concerned with investigating the interplay of genetic, psychosocial, and developmental risk factors, and showed how psychosocial influences on mental disorder could be investigated in a rigorous fashion. His areas of study include maternal deprivation, schooling influences, and the effects of early severe deprivation, such as that experienced by Romanian orphans adopted into Britain. His studies of autism showed that it was a neurodevelopmental rather than psychogenic disorder, with important genetic factors. The interplay between genetic, social and developmental factors underpins a

large area of the Institute's work and has produced some of its most ground-breaking research.

Professor Sir David Goldberg (b 1934), Head of the Department of Psychiatry from 1993 to 1999, and adviser on Mental Health to the Chief Medical Officer from 1989 to 1993, is known internationally for his contribution to the understanding of mental health services, especially at the primary care level and in the assessment of common health disorders.

Schizophrenia

The Division of Psychological Medicine and Psychiatry has international expertise in schizophrenia and bipolar disorder and is best known for helping establish the neurodevelopmental hypothesis of schizophrenia and for defining environmental risk factors for schizophrenia such as obstetric events and cannabis use, especially heavy use in adolescents.

Researchers at King's have linked cannabis use with the development of schizophrenia.

Post-traumatic stress

The IoP's Department of Psychology and the Maudsley's Centre for Anxiety Disorders and Trauma is one of the world's leading centres in anxiety disorders and post-traumatic stress. It has developed influential cognitive approaches to the understanding and treatment of anxiety disorders, leading to programmes of treatment for panic disorder, hypochondriasis, social phobia, and post-traumatic stress disorder which have proved to be significantly more effective than standard forms of treatment such as relaxation training or medication.

ADHD

Research on Attention Deficit Hyperactivity Disorder (ADHD) has been pioneered by the Department of Child & Adolescent Psychiatry. One recent study has demonstrated that ADHD has a physical basis: researchers found that certain parts of the brain in children with ADHD are under-active, especially in an area involving the frontal lobes and basal ganglia, which normally work to inhibit inappropriate responses. The research shows that there is a distinction between ordinary bad behaviour and ADHD and suggests that adults as well as children need to be treated. The Department's research has also shown that children suffering from ADHD are four times more likely to have mental health problems when they grow up than other children. Children who display extreme symptoms of impulsiveness,

inattention and restlessness are more likely to develop an anti-social adjustment, and more likely to show various aspects of personality dysfunction in later adolescence and adult life.

Down's syndrome and Alzheimer's

Researchers from the IoP's Department of Psychological Medicine announced in 2005 that they had identified a molecule that could be targeted to treat cognitive impairment in people with Down's syndrome. The study found that people with Down's syndrome have higher levels of myo-inositol in their brains than people without the condition, and that increased levels of this molecule are associated with reduced intellectual ability. The researchers also suspect that high levels of myo-inositol could play a role in predisposing people with Down's syndrome to early-onset Alzheimer's disease. The molecule is known to promote the formation of amyloid plaques – a hallmark of Alzheimer's. Current studies are exploring whether the concentration of myo-inositol in the brains of people with Down's syndrome can be reduced to treat this disorder.

Neurodegeneration

The IOP has a multidisciplinary approach to the molecular mechanisms of neurodegeneration in Alzheimer's disease and other neurodegenerative disorders, (see page 39) particularly motor neurone disease and the tauopathies. Recent findings include

Researchers at the Institute of Pychiatry have linked Down's syndrome to early-onset Alzheimer's disease.

new mechanisms that regulate processing of the amyloid precursor protein and novel phosphorylation sites on tau. These have led to the identification of new drug targets. One translation into the clinic to test a possible therapy and conduct clinical trials has resulted in the only approved treatment for motor neurone disease (Riluzole), which acts by modifying glutamate transmission.

Arnold Beckett OBE
(b 1920)

Sir James Black OM FRS
(b 1924)

From test-tube to treatment: pharmaceutical sciences

Heart disease, cancer and neurodegenerative disorders are increasingly prevalent in our ageing society.

Research at King's to develop new treatments for such conditions and understand their mechanisms of action has a long and productive history. Sir James Black, (b 1924) the Nobel laureate, and Arnold Beckett, (b 1920) both emeritus Professors of Pharmacology at King's College London, were revolutionary thinkers who paved the way for analytical pharmacology with their work on drug development. Analytical pharmacology is a discipline that is now well established and thrives at King's. The breadth of expertise means that novel drug targets are continually being identified, designed and developed for delivery to patients.

James Black and beta-blockers

When James Black began his work on adrenaline receptor antagonists in the 1950s, the most common treatment for angina pectoris was nitroglycerine which relieved symptoms by causing arteries to dilate. However, subsequent medications developed to increase coronary blood flow were ineffective until Black applied his analytical thinking and discovered a new generation of treatments for high blood pressure and heart disease.

Black's approach was, and is still, to use his understanding of how cells communicate with one another to work out how best to design a new drug. He knew heart rate is determined by the autonomic nervous system and that it could be reduced by sympathetic blockade. He also had the notion that adrenaline could reduce the amount of oxygen reaching the heart tissue via its anoxiating action. This meant that increases in cardiac power could lead to a decrease in cardiac metabolic efficiency.

These observations led Black to his Nobel prize-winning concept that blocking the action of the sympathetic hormones adrenaline and noradrenaline on the heart could help control angina. Anti-adrenaline compounds were already available in 1958, when Black's interests were aroused. However, they reduced blood pressure without affecting tachycardia (rapid heart beat) and isoprenaline, the synthetic derivative of noradrenaline, produced some of the effects of the natural hormone, but not others. This led researchers to think that there were two classes of adrenaline receptors, and Black set out to find an antagonist of the newly identified beta-receptors. Whilst working at ICI

A Nobel distinction

Sir James Black (**below, left**) was awarded the Nobel Prize in Physiology or Medicine in 1988 for the development of two major families of drugs: beta-blockers for the treatment of coronary heart disease, high blood pressure and heart failure, and also the anti-ulcer histamine receptor blocking drugs, including the best-selling Tagamet.

in the early 1960s Black and his team identified a suitable compound that blocked the action of adrenaline, and propranolol the first beta-blocker, was born. He later used a similar approach to identify the equally revolutionary anti-histimine receptor drugs that are used to treat peptic ulcers.

Black was Professor of Analytical Pharmacology and ran an academic unit at King's during the 1980s and fondly reflects on his time at King's in intellectual terms as 'the most productive years of my life'. He is still actively involved in drug development and is Chair of the James Black Foundation, a not-for-profit group of scientists engaged in new drug research based in London.

Novel methods in pharmacology

Arnold Beckett became a senior lecturer, and later Professor, in Pharmaceutical Chemistry at the Chelsea Department of Pharmacy (now part of King's) in 1951. He had trained as a pharmacist and during the war worked on the chemistry of high explosives. In 1956 he spent a year at Smith Kline and French in Philadelphia where he developed an interest in analgesics. He recognized the importance of stereo-chemical features of molecules that had analgesic activity and realized that the analgesic action and addiction liability could be separated – an important observation that informed development of non-addictive pain-killers.

To understand drug metabolism fully, Beckett realized

Detecting drug abuse in sport

Arnold Beckett is pictured (**above, right**) in 1980 working on the equipment used for detecting anabolic steroids. In 1985 King's College London Drug Control Centre became one of a handful in the world to be accredited by the International Olympic Committee. The Centre aims to keep one step ahead of athletes who abuse drugs to enhance their performance. The Centre is part

the need to study pharmaceutical compounds in humans. He set out to develop new analytical methods that would allow researchers to study analgesics, amphetamines, anti-histamines and their metabolites in the small concentrations present in body fluids. When drug abuse in sport became a problem in the 1960s Beckett and his team already had the tools in place to test samples from athletes. During the 1965 'Milk Race', a UK based cycling event, Beckett was invited to carry out tests on the contestants. The results showed that members of one team had been using stimulants and they were disqualified. In 1967 when a cyclist died during the Tour de France after using amphetamines, the need for regulation of drug use in sport was finally recognized. Immediately Beckett's expertise and analytical tests were in demand, and when the Medical Commission of the International Olympic Committee was set up, Beckett was asked to join. Similar invitations

of the Analytical Science Research Group at King's and is currently involved in a government commissioned inquiry into increased use of the anabolic-androgenic steroid nandrolone in sport. It is built on the intellectual foundations laid down by Arnold Beckett, who was made a member of the Olympic Order for his contributions to the regulation of drug use in international sports.

followed from other sports organizing bodies as the unique nature of his expertise became apparent. Beckett's sporting associations were recognised by the International Olympic Committee in 1980 when he was made a member of the Olympic Order. He was awarded an OBE in 1985 and continues to be an honorary member of many international pharmaceutical and scientific associations

Pharmaceutical sciences at King's today

King's has built an international reputation for pharmaceutical research, applying Black's analytical approach and encompassing a wide range of expertise that allows researchers to gain an understanding of the human pathological state and to employ this knowledge to discover, design, develop and deliver drugs to patients.

Discovery and design

To identify new drug targets and active pharmaceutical compounds, researchers in the drug discovery team use a variety of approaches; pharmacognosy – the study of natural products, medicinal (synthetic) chemistry and molecular genetics.

Researchers at King's, in collaboration with the Jodrell Labs at the Royal Botanical Gardens at Kew, have been testing extracts from plants from around the world. Over 100 bioassays are available via the Centre of Bioactivity Screening of Natural Products and can be used to identify compounds from medicinal plants that have potential as therapeutic agents. Such assays have shown that the indole alkaloids harmane and harmaline stimulate release of dopamine brain striatal cells. This may explain why plants containing these compounds have been used as traditional remedies for Parkinsonian symptoms. Many plants used in traditional medicine have anti-cancer properties and several from South East Asia are being tested at King's. The rhizome of a vegetable called galangal that is grown and eaten in Thailand and Malaysia has a reputation as an anti-cancer therapy. Researchers at King's have found it contains an enzyme that protects cells against carcinogens.

Scientists in the Medicinal Chemistry Group design and develop orally active iron-chelators such as Deferipone, a compound that is now extensively used as a main line treatment for thalassaemia. Other powerful iron-chelators designed at King's are in pre-clinical development for use as treatments for neurodegenerative disease and cancer. Researchers in the molecular genetics group are also developing anti-cancer therapies using the cellular protein Hsp90 as a target. This so-called chaperone protein is essential for activating other proteins in the cell such as oncogenic kinases that are involved in cancer. One Hsp90 inhibitor is now in phase II clinical trials.

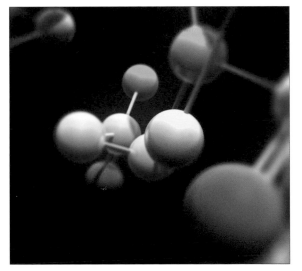

Model of part of the molecule of hepcidin, a hormone produced in the liver which controls body iron levels. It acts by binding to the iron-efflux protein (Ireg) on the duodenal epithelial cells, which was identified and cloned at King's.

Development and delivery

The Drug Delivery Group at King's is looking for novel and non-invasive ways to deliver treatments to patients, such as via inhalation and through the skin. As well as delivering medicines to the lungs, pulmonary delivery can be used as an alternative to oral administration for proteins and peptides that are required systemically. Inhaled insulin is under development and DNAse-1 for use in cystic fibrosis.

King's researchers have also developed a topical cream to treat schistosomiasis, a condition caused by a parasitic worm that affects 200 million people worldwide. Using skin donated by people having plastic surgery, the cream was found to prevent the parasite's larvae penetrating skin for up to 48 hours. If used widely the cream could be enough to slow the spread of disease. A cultured full-thickness skin alternative is being developed to study the structure, function and permeability of skin in order to find new ways to drive compounds through the skin, such as needle-less injection.

Partnerships with industry

To ensure that new treatments reach patients, King's collaborates with industrial partners on a number of levels, from licensing intellectual property to developing clinical trials, and setting up spin-out companies. One of King's spin-outs is Proximagen Neuroscience PLC which was established in 2003 and in 2005 won the *Times Higher* 'Business initiative of the year' award. Proximagen researchers are currently working on a brain protein that helps protect nerve cells to provide a target for treatment of neuro-degenerative disorders such as Alzheimer's and Parkinson's disease.

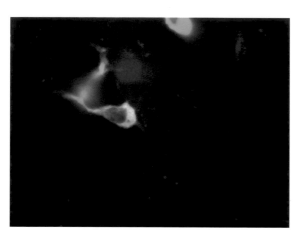

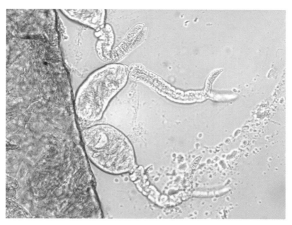

Below Larvae of Schistosoma japonicum penetrating human skin. From the entrance site the larvae spread in the blood stream to become mature parasites, mainly in the liver, kidneys and bladder. The resulting disease can be fatal. Preventing schistomasiasis is an important public health problem in tropical countries where over 200 million people are afflicted. Preventing infection at the stage of skin penetration should prove simple and cheap.

Above Inclusion bodies in degenerating nerve cells from a model of Parkinson's disease. The development of new drugs such as monoamine reuptake inhibitors promises to improve the treatment of Parkinson's disease.

Fingerprints that 'talk' – new forensic methods

Before too long, fingerprints may be more than just a way to identify a person; they may also identify what beauty products that person uses, or illicit substances they abuse.

Scientists at King's are developing ways to analyse trace substances in fingerprints and examine changes over time to look for characteristic patterns particular to an individual. The team hopes the method can be used to detect, amongst other things, drugs of abuse that could help police build a profile of an offender. It could also be developed as a non-invasive medical screening test.

The team is also developing ways to detect minute amounts of drugs in tissues and body fluids. Researchers hope the new methods can be used to solve serious crimes such as date-rape and non-accidental poisoning of children, where forensic evidence is often difficult to obtain.

Richard Mead FRS
(1673-1754)

Sir Samuel Wilks FRS
(1824-1911)

Lord Lister OM FRS
(1827 -1912)

Florence Nightingale OM
(1820-1910)

Sir John Simon FRS
(1816 -1904)

Infection: fighting the age-old enemy

In the 1860s Louis Pasteur's identification of the microscopic organisms that caused fermentation and putrefaction was a breakthrough in understanding infection. However, even before the mechanisms of transmission were properly understood, King's had made important advances in the control of infection in the operating theatre, the ward and the wider world.

Infectious disease remains a major cause of death in the developing world, and the area of South London served by Guy's, King's College and St Thomas' Hospitals suffers from some of the highest rates of infectious disease in the country. Research at King's today recognises two of the newest challenges posed by the ever-changing face of infectious disease – human immunodeficiency virus (HIV) and methicillin resistant staphylococci (MRSA). HIV is a devastating disease with 40 million globally affected. In 2005 alone there were five million new cases and three million deaths. Identifying the mechanisms of HIV infection, its treatment and prevention are the core of current infectious diseases research.

Early work on infection

For centuries, diseases with a high mortality such as plague, smallpox, syphilis and tuberculosis were made more terrifying by the mystery of how they were transmitted. The scientific approach adopted by St Thomas' physician Richard Mead (1673-1754) stands out from a history of quack remedies, astrological theories and charms against infection. His *Short Discourse Concerning Pestilential Contagion and Methods to be Used to Prevent it* was commissioned by the government in 1720 in response to a further threat of plague. At its peak, the plague in 1665 killed 6,000 people a week. The statement helped to alleviate general panic and made a number of practical and theoretical innovations, such as the advice to separate the sick from the healthy (rather than quarantining whole households) and the observation cient; the only Use of which is to observe whether any dye among them. For *Infection* may be preserved so long in Cloaths, in which it is once lodged, that as much, nay more of it, if Sickness continues in the Ship, may be brought on Shore at the End than at the beginning of the 40 Days: Unless a new *Quarentine* be begun every time any Person dies; which might not end, but with the Destruction of the whole Ship's Crew.

If there has been any *Contagious* Distemper in the Ship; The *Sound* Men should leave their Cloaths; which should be burnt; the Men washed and shaved; and having fresh Cloaths, should stay in the *Lazaretto* 30 or 40 Days. The reason of this is, because Persons may be recovered from a Disease themselves, and yet retain
Matter

Mead and the Plague

The plague of 1665 killed more than 100,000 people. In 1720 Richard Mead was commissioned to write his *Short Discourse Concerning Pestilential Contagion and Methods to be Used to Prevent it* with recommendations of limiting the highly contagious disease which included the advice that fabric could transmit the plague.

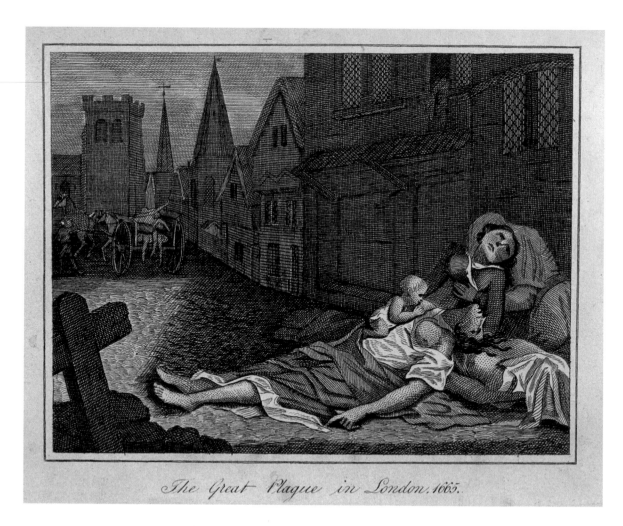

The Great Plague in London. 1665.

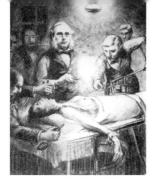
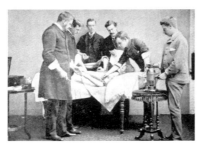

that fabrics could transmit plague (although the role of fleas was not yet known) leading to an early theory of contagion.

Mead turned his attention to smallpox in the following year, when he conducted trials of smallpox inoculations among condemned prisoners at Newgate Prison. His report on these trials (1747) helped to establish the practice of inoculation in England.

In the following century, Samuel Wilks (1824-1911), a physician at Guy's Hospital, was the first to observe that tertiary syphilis affected not only the internal organs such as liver, stomach and lungs, but also the skin.

Lister and antiseptic surgery

Until the early twentieth century, all surgical procedures carried a high risk of death. Limbs injured by compound fracture were usually amputated due to fear of gangrene developing, yet half the cases still died. Abdominal surgery carried such a high risk of mortality that apart from ovariotomy, it was banned at King's College Hospital. It was thought that despite technical accomplishment, surgery on the chest, abdomen and brain would never be the domain of a surgeon's knife. Joseph Lister (1827-1912) during his fifteen years at King's, developed his practice of antiseptic surgery which changed this outlook for the future of surgery.

In 1853, following medical training at University College London, Lister went to Edinburgh to take up a surgical post at the Royal Infirmary. In 1860 he was appointed Professor of Surgery at Glasgow Infirmary.

It was during this time that Lister began to investigate the implications of Pasteur's germ theory. Convinced that putrefaction was caused by airborne bacteria, he used carbolic acid-soaked bandages on wounds to create a barrier against infection. In 1867 he reported in *The Lancet* that of 11 cases of compound fracture so treated, nine had recovered – an excellent result for the time.

Lister was appointed Professor of Surgery at King's College London in 1877 and continued to develop antisepsis at King's College Hospital. On accepting the professorship he made it a condition that he should bring with him his house surgeon, William Watson Cheyne, a senior assistant, John Stewart, and two dressers, W M Dobie and James Altham, in order that his antiseptic methods could be carried out to his specification. He made surgeons wash their hands and instruments in carbolic acid before and after operations, wear clean gloves, swab incisions with carbolic and introduced carbolic sprays into the operating theatre. There was great resistance to these changes from a profession which had worn blood-soaked frock-coats as a mark of honour, as well as objections to the harsh effects of the carbolic acid which left surgeons with cracked skin.

Cheyne was an active supporter of Lister's theories and contributed to them being recognised by the profession. In 1882 he wrote *Antiseptic Surgery: its Principles, Practice, History and Results* which was described by *The Lancet* as 'a starting-point for the more general adoption of Mr Lister's treatment'.

Lister's theory and practices gradually gained support from surgeons and by the mid 1880s there was a rapid increase in the use of his antiseptic techniques. This made possible more advanced lifesaving surgery, including brain and abdominal surgery (Lister was the second man in England to operate on a brain tumour). The technical knowledge already existed but practice had been defeated up to this point because of post operative sepsis.

Lister finally abandoned the spray in 1887 however the influence of his theories was convincing. By 1910 post operative mortality for major operations reduced from 40 per cent to less than three per cent and Lister's principle – that bacteria must never gain entry to an operation wound – remains a basic principle of surgery to this day. Such was his contribution to the profession that surgery is often described as 'before Lister and after Lister'.

'Lord Lister was the greatest material benefactor the world has ever known. He saved more lives than all the wars and all the ages have thrown away'.

Lord Moynihan

Heaf test

Frederick Heaf

Florence Nightingale's war on dirty hospitals

'True nursing ignores infection, except to prevent it' wrote Florence Nightingale (1820-1910) in 1859 in *Notes on Nursing*.

Nightingale had been shocked by the filth, overcrowding and inadequate food provided in military hospitals during the Crimean War in 1854 (see pages 105-106).

On her return, she found conditions little better in English hospitals. Nightingale confidently brought her experiences of the Crimea to the task of reforming hospitals.

Her *Notes on Nursing* redefined the job of nursing as a respectable profession, stressing discipline and cleanliness, and a year later she founded the world's first professional nursing school at St Thomas' Hospital. Nightingale also made recommendations for the design of hospitals and the layout of wards, and pioneered the use of record-keeping, statistics and epidemiological analysis to judge the success of her methods.

These improvements in hospital practice and conditions were paralleled by public health reforms, the 1866 Sanitary Act which improved sanitary drainage (enforcing connection of all new houses to a sewer) and defined overcrowding as a nuisance, and the Public Health Act of 1875. Both acts were impelled by Sir John Simon (1816-1904), who trained at St Thomas' Hospital, was Demonstrator of

The Heaf test

Frederick Heaf (1894-1973) qualified at St Thomas' and worked at a specialist tuberculosis sanatoria before being appointed as medical officer in charge of the anti-tuberculosis service for London.

While Professor of Tuberculosis at the University of Wales, Heaf devised and validated the standard multiple puncture 'Heaf Test' which gives a quantitative assessment of tuberculin sensitivity from a single skin test. This test was used in the UK until 2005.

Anatomy at King's College, London and surgeon at King's College Hospital, before becoming the first Medical Officer of Health for London (see pages 49-50).

One of Simon's great achievements was making smallpox vaccination compulsory for children in 1870.

HIV

King's continues its legacy of research into infectious diseases. The Department of Infectious Diseases is focusing its research on understanding and finding treatments for HIV, now one of the world's most devastating infectious diseases. There is a particular

opportunity, and responsibility, for King's to investigate HIV. The College's local area of South London has the highest rate of HIV incidence in the UK.

Unlocking the body's resistance to HIV

Understanding the molecular events affecting HIV-host interactions leading to the basic event in HIV infection – the invasion of T-cells by the virus – is crucial for the development of effective drugs and vaccines.

A key insight, relevant to other virus infections not just HIV, came with the description by King's researchers in 2003 of a previously unknown mechanism in human cells to protect against viral infection. HIV produces a protein, Vif, essential for the virus to enter cells and replicate. How Vif did this was unknown until the discovery of a gene, CEM15, which produces a protein (APOBEC3G, a cytosine deaminase) which renders HIV non-infectious. Vif counteracts this beneficial gene and its product. This significant finding could lead to new treatments for HIV – by blocking the action of Vif, CEM15 would be allowed to work properly and prevent HIV replicating and spreading. Work is ongoing to identify substances that bind to and inhibit Vif in the cell, and defining its structure and precise modes of action.

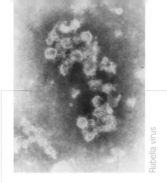
Rubella virus

Jenny Best

Jangu Banatvala

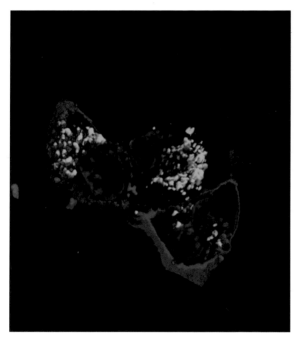

Diagnosing rubella

1964 witnessed a worldwide rubella epidemic leading to many cases of congenital rubella syndrome. The virus had been isolated in 1962 and the race was on to develop new techniques for the rapid diagnosis of rubella in pregnancy and the development of rubella vaccines. Jenny Best and Jangu Banatvala came to St Thomas' Hospital Medical School in 1965, where they developed a technique for rapid diagnosis by detection of rubella-specific IgM. Collaboration with June Almeida led to the first characterisation of rubella virus by electron microscopy (see picture), while studies of immune response to rubella vaccines using nurses and medical students as volunteers helped to confirm the efficacy of the current vaccine strain. Rubella vaccination was introduced to the UK in 1970 and the incidence of congenital rubella syndrome fell thereafter from 200-300 to an average of four cases a year between 1991 and 1995.

Non-progressive HIV

As HIV-infected populations are monitored it has become clear that there are groups of patients who do not progress to AIDS. Detailed dissection of the immune response of these patients to the virus is another tool to understand the interaction between host and virus. A 12 year study of non-progressors by King's researchers with collaborators in other centres has defined several novel immunological features in these individuals. Examples are an association between HLA alleles (DQ6) and the rate of decline of CD4 T-cells, and the selection of a unique T-cell receptor by HIV-specific T-cells.

The subtypes of HIV also influence the disease, and an epidemiological study of these and their effect on progression and response to treatment is ongoing in South London.

Drug therapy for HIV

The outcome of drug therapy is variable, and King's is collaborating in two large UK-based studies analysing factors affecting patients' responses to treatment. Among those described are the rate of viral rebound after reduction in HIV load related to the antiviral drugs used, and the long-term probability of detecting HIV-1 resistance.

The clinical trials programme at King's College and St Thomas' Hospitals is evaluating novel antiviral agents such as the new fusion inhibitor, Fuezon, which prevents fusion of the virus with the cell; an antagonist of the CCR5 chemokine receptor; and new protease inhibitors effective against drug resistant isolates.

Black Africans and Caribbeans are diagnosed significantly later than the general population and an MRC-funded study at ten UK centres including King's is examining the sociodemographic, behavioural and laboratory factors affecting the impact of HIV and its treatment on this section of the population.

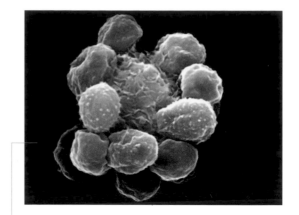

Vaccines

The ultimate aim to rid the world of HIV is the production of an effective vaccine.

Work to date has shown that DNA HIV vaccines are safe and well tolerated. An alloimmune HIV vaccine is undergoing evaluation. Vaccination by the mucosal route, mimicking the natural method of infection and involving the regional lymph nodes, is being evaluated.

King's is a member of the Centre for HIV-AIDS Immunology at the USA National Institutes of Health, which was set up to examine the immunological barriers to vaccine development and to test new vaccines.

MRSA – in the footsteps of Lister

MRSA (methicillin resistant staphylococci) has become a household name as a hospital acquired, sometimes fatal, infectious disease. In the UK in 2003, 953 patients died from this infection per annum, and the reported incidence of infection is 7,000 annually. Its descriptive name underlines its challenge as it is resistant to the range of antibiotics used to treat staphylococcal infections; this is a return therefore to the preantibiotic era for patients infected with MRSA.

Work at King's, based at Guy's and St Thomas' Hospitals, is using molecular analysis of MRSA in a number of ways to reduce its impact. Rapid molecular typing methods have been developed to analyse and control outbreaks, to identify high level mupirocin resistance in MRSA strains and for rapid detection of MRSA in blood cultures. With colleagues at St George's Hospital the genetic basis of pathogenicity in different MRSA strains is being examined.

Researchers have shown that the contaminated hospital environment is a source of cross infection as MRSA can survive on dry surfaces for many weeks. Conventional cleaning fails to decontaminate these surfaces but gassing with H2O2 is effective.

From 2004, highly virulent community strains of MRSA with a predilection for children have developed and studies of the molecular epidemiology and control of these organisms have begun.

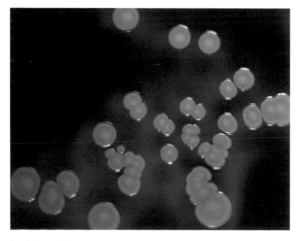

Staphylococcal aurens growing on culture medium. Its usual strains can cause serious infections of wounds, skin and lungs. These will be more difficult to eradicate and more life threatening if the staphylococcus is MRSA.

World's first infectious diseases BioBank

In 2005, King's announced plans for the world's first infectious diseases BioBank to be housed at Guy's Hospital. This library of clinical materials containing DNA and RNA samples and live frozen white blood cells will support King's research in HIV, MRSA, hepatitis B and malaria. King's location in South London is ideal for studying agents of infection, both local and international, as the catchment area from which the BioBank will draw its samples are ethnically diverse, mobile and impoverished – factors which allow infectious diseases to flourish and new agents to emerge.

Thomas Hodgkin
(1798-1866)

Sir Samuel Wilks FRS
(1824-1911)

Leonard Dudgeon
(1876-1938)

Sir Hedley Atkins
(1905-1983)

Peter Gorer FRS
(1907-1961)

Michael Hutt (1922-2000)

Making inroads: cancer studies & research

Cancer research at King's and its constituent institutions can be traced back more than 100 years to a time when clinical pathology was barely a recognized discipline.

Since then it has been the training ground for several prominent researchers including Hedley Atkins (1905-1983) and Peter Gorer (1907-1961). The specific aims of cancer research at King's today are as varied as cancer itself, and range from the psychosocial implications of a cancer diagnosis to the protein-protein interactions that take place between individual cancer cells. All have the common aim of improving clinical outcomes for people with cancer, and many studies build on fundamentals laid down by their predecessors.

Thomas Hodgkin (1798-1866) was the first contributor from King's with his eponymous description of enlargement of the internal lymph nodes and spleen. Samuel Wilks (1824-1911) described the same condition some years later, but it was he who named it after Hodgkin. He also made the first description of lymphatic leukaemia.

Leonard Dudgeon (1876-1938) was one of the first people to recognise the close relationship between pathology and clinical medicine, and can be thought of as King's first cancer researcher. He qualified as a physician at St Thomas' Hospital in 1901 and later became head of the Louis Jenner Clinical Laboratory where he studied the pathology of malignant cells. During his 35-year career at St Thomas', Dudgeon pioneered cytology by developing methods for rapidly diagnosing tumours using smears of body fluids and tumours. He was among the first to diagnose lung cancer from single malignant cells.

Like Dudgeon, Hedley Atkins, a pioneering breast cancer researcher, was loyal to the hospital that trained him and spent most of his working life at Guy's. He graduated in 1932 and became the first professor of surgery at Guy's in 1961. He pioneered controlled clinical trials to test treatments for breast cancer including those that compared the benefits of local removal of the tumour (lumpectomy) with radical breast surgery (mastectomy). He was one of the first to realise that the complex nature of breast disease meant that outcomes could be improved if surgery was accompanied by other treatments such as radiotherapy and chemotherapy, and to recognize the influence of hormones on prognosis. His achievements in the study

Sir Richard Doll

St Thomas' alumnus Sir Richard Doll was a UN prize-winner for his research into the causes and control of cancer. Based on his extensive population studies in the 1950s he was the first to suggest and later prove, that there was a direct link between smoking and lung cancer.

of breast pathology are commemorated to this day in the Hedley Atkins Breast Unit and Breast Pathology Tissue Bank.

Another graduate of Guy's Hospital, Professor Peter Gorer (1907-1961), became a key contributor to the study of organ and tissue graft rejection and tumour immunology. He developed antibodies in inbred mice that for the first time distinguished normal and malignant lymphoid cells serologically. But it was his studies to define the antigenic composition of tumours and what rendered them transplantable between strains of mice that made a major contribution to our understanding of one of the fundamentals of immunology – histocompatability antigens (see pages 31-34).

In the 1960s Michael Hutt (1922-2000), Professor of Geographical Pathology at St Thomas', began work into how environmental factors influence cancer incidence. He worked with Denis Burkitt in East Africa studying the epidemiology and environmental risk factors for Burkitt's lymphoma and Kaposi's sarcoma. He also established one of the first cancer registers. St Thomas' alumnus Sir Richard Doll (1912-2005), is however, the most famous figure in the field of environmental risk of cancer. His work with Austin Bradford Hill linked smoking and lung cancer; an association first made public in 1951. He was awarded the UN prize for outstanding research into the causes and control of cancer.

Cancer research at King's today

Cancer research at King's ranges from studies to understand pyschosocial aspects of cancer to those exploring the molecular events that take place in individual cancer cells. And although much current research exploits cutting edge technology such as proteomics and optical imaging, the legacy of early cancer researchers lives on in resources such as the Hedley Atkins Breast Pathology Tissue Bank and the Thames Cancer Registry. These provide essential material and data for today's cancer researches.

Breast cancer

One in nine women will develop breast cancer at some point in their lives. Scientists in the Breast Cancer Biology Laboratory are studying the changes that occur when breast cells become cancerous. They have identified a protein called PLU-1 that is expressed in the nucleus of breast cancer cells and may be a cancer antigen that could be targeted using immunotherapy. The team is also exploring MUC-1 mucin – a protein that is upregulated in breast cancer and other cancer cells – as a target for cancer immunotherapy.

Studies to identify genes involved in susceptibility to cancer and other common diseases are complemented by work to understand the role that the encoded proteins play in disease. The BRCA-1 gene has been identified as an early onset familial breast/ovarian cancer predisposition gene, and researchers are studying BRCA-1 mutations that lead to altered function which will help them understand the clinical significance of these changes (see also page 29).

The Cancer Cell Motility and Imaging group use changes in protein expression within cells to explore metastasis, the primary cause of death in cancer. Thus, studies to understand how cancers spread should identify novel targets for effective therapies and medicines. Both cancer cell growth and killing of cancer cells by the immune system involve a complex series of protein interactions that signal changes within the cell. Thanks to advanced optical techniques developed by researchers at King's, these interactions can now be studied in intricate detail, and in real time. This technique – known as near infra-red multiphoton real time resolved imaging – examines protein expression in breast tissue. Using the technique to measure differences in B1 integrin cluster expression, ductal carcinoma in-situ – a non-invasive cancer – can be distinguished from invasive breast cancer. Researchers now plan to study expression of a protein called Ezrin (see picture, right) that they have identified as a key component of tumour metastasis and a potential disease target. By identifying protein clusters involved in metastasis it should be possible to target the clusters and reverse the interaction to halt cancer spread. The team now plans to develop the technique further to study expression of all cellular proteins – a technique they call optical proteomics.

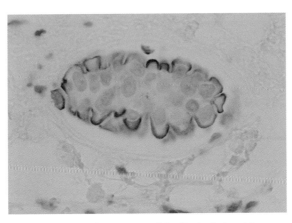

Above Showing a mass of tumour cells migrating through the lymph vessel of an individual patient with invasive breast cancer.

Below Showing Ezrin protein interacting with a serine/threonine kinase known as protein kinase C at the edge of a growing breast cancer cell.

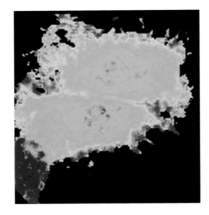

Psychology

A multi-professional group is exploring the psychological and psychosocial aspects of cancer. Women with breast cancer are being studied for the effectiveness of psycho-educational intervention to prevent delays in presentation and so improve survival rates. To combat the psychological effects of cancer the group is evaluating the treatment of psychological morbidity and physical symptoms. A different but relevant approach is the group's work on improving the working lives of health professionals in the cancer field, so improving the care they give to patients.

Myeloma

The first diagnosis of multiple myeloma, a bone marrow cancer, was made at St Thomas' Hospital in 1844. Understanding why myeloma patients vary so greatly in their clinical responses to therapy is now a primary research focus in the Department of Haematology and Molecular Medicine. Researchers in the Department, which also hosts the UK's largest haemopoietic stem cell transplantation centre, are looking for ways to exploit the body's own immune system in treating myeloma. They are exploring a novel antigen specific vaccination strategy and also have approval to begin the first immune gene therapy trial in acute myeloid leukaemia in patients with a poor prognosis.

Skin cancer

Skin cancer is the body's normal long term response to sunlight. There are two critical steps in skin cancer: DNA photodamage that results in mutation, and UV-radiation induced immunosuppression that prevents skin tumour rejection. These changes can together lead to aberrant cell growth. Researchers in the Photobiology Unit at King's have established a bank of primary fibroblasts and keratinocytes from normal donors with different skin types in order to study the events that lead to skin cancer. They have discovered that, using solar simulating radiation (SSR), sun-sensitive skin types are more readily immunosuppressed by SSR than sun-resistant skin types and that sunscreens are less able to prevent UV radiation-induced immuno-suppression than they are to prevent sunburn.

The St John's Institute of Dermatology is a referral centre for cutaneous lymphoma, and is assessing various treatments for this uncommon malignancy. These include anti-CD4 antibody and pilot studies of autologous stem cell transplantation in advanced cases. In collaboration with the Division of Immunology, Infection and Inflammatory Disease, abnormalities of T-cell activation signalling pathways have been demonstrated.

Epidemiology and health services research

The Thames Cancer Registry at King's is the largest population-based cancer registry in Europe and provides an important data resource for research into cancer epidemiology. Apart from descriptive epidemiology and aetiological studies of events preceding diagnosis, it can explore variations in cancer services provision and related outcomes between different parts of the country, and so make an important contribution to cancer services planning.

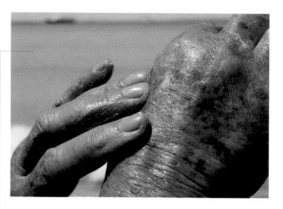

The hidden danger of sunscreen
The need for protection against the hazardous effects of the sun are well known, but the King's Photobiology Unit has shown that even sunscreen protection against sunburn may not make exposure safe. Research has demonstrated that a sunscreen's ability to prevent UVR-induced immunosuppression may well be very much lower than its ability to prevent sunburn, in which case sunscreen use might enhance skin cancer risk by giving a false sense of security.

Dame Cicely Saunders OM
(1918-2005)

At the end of life: Dame Cicely Saunders & palliative care

King's and its associated hospitals have a distinguished history in pioneering palliative care, from the early foundations of St Thomas' and Guy's Hospitals to the prodigious accomplishments of St Thomas' alumna Dame Cicely Saunders, and from the distinction of the current King's Department of Palliative Care to the forthcoming Cicely Saunders Institute of Palliative Care.

In 1967 Dame Cicely Saunders (1918-2005), an alumna of St Thomas', founded the first modern hospice and initiated the worldwide modern hospice movement, and in 2002 she founded The Cicely Saunders Foundation to take forward research and education in this area.

The word 'hospice' dates from Roman times, meaning a place of care and refuge, and it took on the sense of being a place specifically for the care of the dying in the late nineteenth century. St Thomas' Hospital began its life as a hospice in both senses, as a refuge run by a religious order for travellers crossing London Bridge, from as early as the sixth century. Guy's Hospital was established in the 1720s as a place for those perceived as being 'incurable', according to the will of Thomas Guy, its founder and first benefactor.

In 2004 The Cicely Saunders Foundation and King's College London announced plans to establish the world's first research centre for palliative care, the Cicely Saunders Institute of Palliative Care.

The modern hospice movement

Palliative care is a specialty that cares for patients with advanced, incurable conditions, providing expertise in the management of symptoms, supporting distressed patients and families, coordinating complex social care, promoting patient choice at the end of life and managing death and bereavement.

Dame Cicely Saunders devoted her life to ensuring that terminally ill people could die with dignity and without pain. She read Philosophy, Politics and Economics at Oxford before coming to St Thomas' to train as a nurse, then as a lady almoner (medical social

The painting by C W Cope RA, 1871, depicts the founder Thomas Guy, the architect Thomas Dance and Dr Richard Mead inspecting a plan of the proposed Guy's Hospital. The hospital was intended for 400 sick persons 'who might not be received into other hospitals from being deemed incurable' and for the care of up to 20 'lunatics'.

worker) and finally as a doctor, qualifying from St Thomas' in 1957. In 1967 she founded St Christopher's Hospice in Sydenham, South London, to provide total and active care for patients with incurable diseases, and this became the model for hospices and palliative care worldwide.

Dame Cicely's belief that dying is a phenomenon 'as natural as being born' was at the heart of a philosophy that sees death as a process that should be life-affirming and free of pain. She transformed the way in which terminally ill patients were looked after. Previously, pain relief had been dealt with as a purely medical issue, and as a nurse she had seen the suffering of patients for hours at a time between doses of pain-killing medication. What Dame Cicely demonstrated was that intermittent reactive sedation of surging pain was far less effective than achieving a steady state in which the dying could still maintain consciousness and even some quality of life. She believed in the importance of allowing patients to control their own treatment, and also recognised the need to work closely with families of the terminally ill.

The change Dame Cicely accomplished in medical attitudes was most notably recognised when the Royal College of Physicians established palliative medicine as a distinct medical specialty in 1987. In 1989 Cicely Saunders received the Order of Merit: the same honour that Florence Nightingale had been the first woman to achieve in 1907.

'It appears to me that many patients feel deserted by their doctors at the end. Ideally the doctor should remain the centre of a team who work together to relieve where they cannot heal, to keep the patient's own struggle within his compass and to bring hope and consolation to the end.'

Dame Cicely Saunders

An academic focus for palliative care

The King's College London Department of Palliative Care was founded in 1996. In this short time, the department has already made leading national and international contributions. In the UK it has shown that in patients with advanced malignancy, black caribbeans have higher levels of symptomatic-related distress, with poorer access to and experience of palliative care than white UK-born patients. In collaboration with the King's Florence Nightingale School of Nursing & Midwifery, the department is developing guidance on supportive and palliative care for cancer patients for the National Institute of Clinical Excellence. This is central to the strategy for supportive care outlined in the Government's National Cancer Plan.

Palliative care is not concerned with cancer alone. The need for palliative care for patients with multiple sclerosis is being evaluated by the Department. The Candle project is also examining the impact of childhood bereavement on school performance and behaviour and the efficacy of multiprofessional intervention.

Understanding and control of pain is an integral part of palliative care. The Pain Clinical Research Hub, a collaboration between King's College London, King's College Hospital and Pfizer Ltd, is using the latest imaging techniques to measure the brain activity of people in pain to obtain objective measurements of pain intensity.

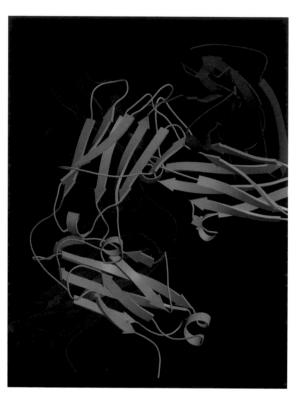

tests. When he started his work with Charles Fletcher at the Pneumoconiosis Research Unit at Cardiff the only lung function test available was vital capacity. They developed tests to measure total lung volume, maximum breathing capacity and gas transfer from the lung using carbon monoxide. Hugh-Jones developed these tests further at King's College Hospital with bronchoscopic measurement of regional ventilation. He also developed a simple standard exercise test. This physiological clinical research laid the foundation for the routine tests used today for assessing patients' lung function.

Ian Cameron (b 1936) led work at St Thomas' Hospital on the central and peripheral nervous control of breathing, the physiological consequences of long-term respiratory failure and the regulation of the pulmonary circulation. The contributions of this group increased the understanding of the pathophysiology of chronic respiratory disease and therefore its management.

Asthma and allergy

One in three of the population has allergy diagnosed at some stage in their lives. Seventy per cent of allergy sufferers have asthma, and many of these have other allergies such as eczema or conjunctivitis.

The underlying abnormality in asthma, the narrowing of the airways, is now well recognised to be a chronic inflammatory disease.

A wide range of cells causing inflammation – eosinophils, neutrophils, mast cells and T-cells – are activated, with consequent damage to the epithelium in the airways. A major research programme is focused on identifying the signals to these cells which recruit and activate them, such as cytokines and prostaglandins. Recent work has also shown that intact platelets play a role in recruiting eosinophils and lymphocytes to the lungs, thus giving another new aspect to possible treatments.

Immunoglobulin E (IgE) starts the inflammatory process by binding to its receptors on mast cells.

Studying the 3D structure of IgE has pointed to a novel way of inhibiting its function. IgE itself has an unusual structure in that its receptor binding regions are acutely bent back on themselves; the molecule has to 'unbend' to bind to its receptor. So instead of attempting to inhibit binding directly, researchers are pursuing an entirely new approach: designing a molecule that will bind to the unattached IgE and prevent it from unbending.

Exploring treatment

Researchers at King's have explored new drugs and different ways of using established drugs in the treatment of asthma, including using low-dose theophylline as an anti-inflammatory and immunomodulating drug, and an antibody which blocks cytokines.

Although the range of drugs for treating asthma means that in 90 per cent of sufferers the disease is adequately controlled, there is great concern about the remainder. A particular problem is resistance to the commonly used steroids. Work undertaken at King's has suggested several different reasons for this; it was recently observed that steroid-resistant T-cells can be transformed to a steroid-sensitive state by oral vitamin D3. This potentially offers a simple way to reduce steroid resistance.

Children and asthma

Pregnant women can influence their offspring's risk of asthma through their diet and the drugs they take. Recent studies at King's have shown that protection against asthma is afforded by selenium, iron, and possibly flavenoids in the maternal diet. On the other hand, paracetamol has been confirmed as a risk factor if taken during pregnancy.

During childhood, infection, known to be a precipitant of asthma attacks, can also be a risk factor for the later development of asthma. Respiratory syncytial virus infection before the age of 5 years doubles the risk of asthma.

Childhood infection can be a risk factor in the later development of asthma.

In children with sickle cell disease, the onset of asthma precedes acute chest syndrome. This implies that effective treatment of asthma may reduce the frequency of this complication of sickle cell disease.

Chronic obstructive pulmonary disease

Cigarette smoking is the major cause of COPD. One effect of smoking demonstrated at King's is its lowering of the numbers of CD4 and CD8 T-cells, central to the immune response, and so it can lead to increased rates of lower respiratory tract infections.

Although the chronic lung damage in COPD is not reversible, one aim of treatment is to maximise the residual lung function; this has been shown to be improved through the non-invasive treatment of Proportional Assist Ventilation.

Constriction of blood vessels and hypertension in the pulmonary circulation are recognized complications of chronic hypoxia, which occurs in COPD. Work at King's has shown that pulmonary endothelium plays a vital role in sustained vasoconstriction. Analysis of the complex molecular actions producing pulmonary vasoconstriction (such as calcium sensitisation and entry) suggests that Trp channels could provide a pharmacological target for the development of pulmonary-specific vasodilators for the treatment of hypoxic pulmonary vasoconstriction.

Bee venom can cause anaphylaxis, with approximately 40 reported deaths since 1992 in the UK. Maurice Lessof (b 1924), Professor of Medicine at Guy's from 1971 to 1989, started the allergy clinic at Guy's in 1968, and treated anaphylaxis due to bee venom by desensitisation for the first time in the UK in 1973.

In 2005, the Medical Research Council-Asthma UK Centre in Allergic Mechanisms of Asthma was established at King's College London and Imperial College London. Allergy has increased three-fold in the last 20 years while asthma affects nine per cent of the population. Medical Research Council Chief Executive, Colin Blakemore on the Centre's announcement said: 'We have the potential to build a world class research centre for asthma and allergy that will deepen our understanding of the allergic mechanisms of asthma and inform the development of new treatments'.

3D map of London produced by King's showing pollution levels, red being high and blue low.

The environment

The link between environmental pollutants and the exacerbation of asthma and COPD is a well known fact. A recent multi-centre European study coordinated by King's has shown the relation between asthma and nitrogen dioxide and nitrous acid, by-products of fossil fuel combustion.

The King's Environmental Research Group measures and predicts pollutant levels in London's air, and investigates the mechanisms that underlie the toxic effects of air pollution and how they impact on public health. It is currently working with University College London to create an online 3D map of London to show how air quality and the health of residents and workers vary from street to street (above). The Lung Biology Research Group looks at pollutants such as ozone, nitrogen dioxide and particulate matter, and the reasons why some individuals are especially sensitive to air pollution.

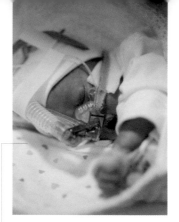

The neonatal lung

Respiratory problems in the newborn, especially premature babies, are common. Work in the neonatal respiratory units at St Thomas' Hospital and King's College Hospital has examined the relationship between the physiology of breathing and resuscitation in the newborn. In the 1940s and 50s, Professor Maureen Young (b 1915), one of the first women to join the Physiology Department at St Thomas' Hospital Medical School, was involved in developing methods of measuring oxygen in the newborn's blood, and with Ian Donald (1910-1987) experimented on improving the design of ventilators. More recently, Anthony Milner (b 1938), at St Thomas' worked on ensuring that neonatal ventilation is based on sound physiological principles and scientific evidence. Validating new ventilation techniques and ventilators and so reducing ventilation-associated complications is an important current area of investigation.

George Owen Rees FRS
(1813-1889)

Frederick W Pavy FRS
(1829-1911)

Robert Daniel Lawrence
(1892-1968)

Lord Butterfield OBE
(1920-2000)

David Pyke CBE
(1921-2001)

Harry Keen CBE
(b 1925)

Victor Parsons
(1929-1995)

Peter Watkins (b 1935)

Peter Sonksen (b 1936)

Improving the diabetic life

Contributions to the understanding of diabetes by George Owen Rees and William Pavy can be traced back to the 1800s.

King's has made continuous significant contributions since the 1920s to the improvement of the diabetic condition, beginning with perfecting the use of insulin. The physiology of insulin and insulin independence for patients have been a major focus since the 1960s. In 2004 the UK's first islet cell transplantation was successfully performed at King's College Hospital, allowing the patient to become insulin independent. King's remains at the forefront of diabetes research as it investigates the prevention of diabetes by a potential vaccine for Type 1 diabetes, with clinical trials beginning in 2006.

Perfecting the use of insulin

Robert Daniel Lawrence (1892-1968) dominated the diabetes scene in the UK from the 1920s. Frederick Banting's and Charles Best's breakthrough discovery of insulin in 1921 gave new hope for the treatment of diabetics and survival beyond the maximum expected four years. Lawrence's work as one of the first UK physicians specialising in diabetology was to investigate the use of insulin as a drug to realise the improvement in prognosis that insulin promised.

Lawrence originally trained as a surgeon, though an accident, followed by a chance diagnosis of diabetes, left an eye permanently damaged and his surgical career no longer viable. Following his diagnosis, for which he was one of the first in the UK to be treated with insulin in 1923, he dedicated his life to the most effective treatments for diabetes. He was appointed physician to the new Department of Diabetes which he established in 1932 at King's College Hospital. Lawrence monitored his own routines, in particular the effects of exercise and diet. With his laboratory assistant HR Miller, also a diabetic, they tested on themselves new batches of insulin before issuing them to patients.

By the end of the Second World War Lawrence had become the leader of diabetes activity in the UK. The Diabetic Department had become the largest in Britain, with an international reputation for research and training and he was the first to establish in 1939 a children's diabetic clinic.

He published *The Diabetic Life* and *The Diabetic ABC*, groundbreaking books for patients and nurses about how to manage diabetes, and with author HG Wells

RD Lawrence made landmark contributions to the proper use of insulin for the treatment of diabetes patients, including diabetic pregnancy.
He was a believer in patient education and empowerment and in 1925 he published The Diabetic Life and The Diabetic ABC. These were groundbreaking texts for patients and health professionals on living with diabetes and managing the illness. The books included practical information including Lawrence's line diet.

HG Wells

GDH Cole

Care for the diabetic community

In the absence of any other organisation to 'watch over the diabetic community' as he referred to it, RD Lawrence, with the fellow diabetes sufferers author HG Wells and economist GDH Cole, in 1934 set up the Diabetic Association. Their aim was to ensure that everyone in the UK could gain access to insulin whatever their financial situation. The charity, now known as Diabetes UK, remains an important provider of patient and professional support and also funds diabetes research throughout the UK.

and economist GDH Cole, had established the Diabetic Association (now Diabetes UK).

Lawrence's work in the treatment of diabetic coma and pregnancy in the diabetic also became a major focus. In the 1950s, with physician Wilfred Oakely and obstetrician Sir John Peel at King's College Hospital, he created the first joint diabetes-pregnancy clinic. Originally describing a fetal mortality of thirty five per cent in the babies of diabetic women they were able to reduce this to fifteen per cent. Work since has further reduced this to five per cent nationwide and the last audit at King's (1997-2002)

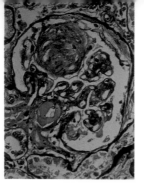

Histology of diabetic nephropathy. Dr Victor Parsons **right** was a pioneer in the dialysis and transplantation of kidney failure in diabetics.

showed a fetal loss rate in pregnancy in women with established diabetes no different from that of the background population.

Lawrence's legacy of investigating the use of insulin continued with Peter Sonksen's (b 1936) work on the the effect of stepped insulin infusions on glucose turnover. This led to the description of low-dose insulin infusion for the treatment of diabetic keto-acidosis from the departments at Guy's, St Thomas' and King's College Hospitals in collaboration with colleagues at Oxford and Newcastle Universities. This method of treatment provided a steadier reduction in glucose levels and a predictable stage at which glucose infusion could be started. It reduced the risk of cerebral oedema and lowered mortality rates.

To improve the delivery of insulin and blood glucose control, Harry Keen (b 1925) and George Alberti (Newcastle) developed continuous subcutaneous insulin infusion which has become the current standard insulin pump therapy worldwide. Current work at Guy's has developed this technique further and conducted trials on its application.

Managing the complications of diabetes

The ironic penalty of patients surviving longer on insulin is the opportunity for complications of diabetes to develop. Coronary artery disease, strokes, chronic renal failure, blindness, peripheral neuropathy and the diabetic foot have become the prime causes of morbidity and death for many diabetics.

A major advance in the management of diabetic patients was the definition of microalbumenuria as a predictor of diabetic renal disease and of cardiovascular risk by Keen and colleagues in the 1960s and 70s.

Today diabetes constitutes the single commonest European cause of kidney failure and King's continues to make major scientific contributions to under-standing its causes, prevention and treatment. In the 1970s Victor Parsons (1929-1995), with his colleague Peter Watkins (b 1935), was a pioneer in the dialysis and transplantation of this condition at a time when most UK renal units were electively not treating diabetics as results were so poor. His perseverance eventually showed that quality and length of survival could be improved to acceptable levels, leading to widespread acceptance of treatment for diabetics.

The renal fibrosis which characterizes the microscopic changes in the diabetic kidney continues to be studied by analyzing the molecular mechanisms causing extracellular matrix production by mesangial cells.

The chemistry of diabetes

Although the ancient Indians knew that blood and urine were sweet in diabetes, Guy's physician George Owen Rees (1813-1889) was the first to document and measure excess sugar in the blood in the 1840s. Frederick W Pavy (1829-1911), a Guy's physician

George Owen Rees **left** in the 1840s was the first to document and measure excess sugar in the blood. In the 1850s Frederick W Pavy **right** was one of the first to realise that acetone and other ketones were a product of diabetic metabolism.

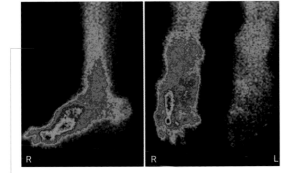

'Every 30 seconds a lower limb is lost somewhere in the world as a consequence of diabetes' (*The Lancet* 2005). Diabetic foot disease is a now world-wide scourge. As long ago as the 1980s the first major diabetic foot clinic was established at King's College Hospital. The concentration of expertise has reduced amputation rates by 50 per cent.

and physiologist, collaborated with Richard Bright and described intermittent proteinuria. He is perhaps best remembered for his prolonged polemic against the views of Claude Bernard with whom he had worked as a young man. He argued that Bernard's claim that the liver stored glucose as glycogen and fed it back into the circulation in the fasting state was entirely misconceived.

In the 1960s John Butterfield (1920-2000) and colleagues at Guy's Hospital studied the effects of insulin, glucagon and therapeutic agents on the diabetic human forearm muscles and described aspects of insulin resistance. He mastered the technique of measuring arterial and venous blood concentrations of glucose, metabolites and hormones in the human forearm circulation along with blood flow measurements. He directly demonstrated evidence for resistance to the effects of insulin in diabetes and also acromegaly and obesity. He extended these observations to arterio-venous differences across the human brain.

Understanding the physiology of islet cells and the mechanisms of insulin secretion has been a major research focus since the 1980s. This has defined the role of the cytoskeleton in exocytosis in beta cells. It has also led to the ability to measure the insulin production *in vitro* by stem cells, tumour cells and harvested human donor pancreatic cells. The last is of obvious use for transplantation.

Population studies

In the early 1960s studies on the epidemiology of early diabetes and evolution of its complications were conducted by Butterfield jointly with Keen and the Guy's academic team in the Bedford Population Study. These long-term studies contributed directly to the formulation of the WHO glycaemic re-definition of diabetes and 'impaired glucose tolerance'. They demonstrated for the first time in a population setting the clear link between glucose intolerance and atherosclerotic disease risk. The study led directly to the first description of 'microalbuminuria' which enabled Keen and colleagues to explore the early mechanisms and prevention of diabetic nephropathy in humans.

David Pyke (1921-2001) began his renowned study of identical twins in the early 1960s. The study became the largest of its kind in the world and showed that monozygous twin pairs were substantially more likely to be concordant for diabetes if they had Type 2 than Type 1 diabetes, confirming that the two types were differently inherited and that environmental 'trigger' factors were clearly necessary to provoke the Type 1 diabetic state. The twins were also used to demonstrate the importance of the HLA constitution in Type 1 as against Type 2 diabetes and the fascinating observations on the potentially very long period of activated autoimmunity in Type 1 before clinical evidence (even minor glucose intolerance) appears. The twin studies also provided one of the first opportunities for the trial of immunosuppression in the very early phases of Type 1. There are still more than 500 pairs who volunteer to take part in this study.

DAFNE (Dose Adjustment for Normal Eating) was pioneered in Germany and introduced to the UK at King's College Hospital in 2000. This programme teaches patients how to adjust insulin doses to fit their lifestyle rather than modify eating and activity to a pre-set insulin regime. This is now the only programme in Type 1 diabetes recommended by NICE.

Cerebral control of metabolism in acute hypoglycaemia

Although euglycaemia is an ideal goal for treating diabetes, it carries the risk of effects on the brain caused by chronic intermittent hypoglycaemia. To investigate this, a collaborative group at King's is investigating the cerebral control of metabolism in acute hypoglycaemia, and also insulin resistant syndromes. It has demonstrated an insulin element to brain glucose metabolism in man which may be relevant to the pathogenesis of obesity and metabolic syndrome.

The increased risk of severe hypoglycaemia in intensively treated Type 1 diabetes has been shown to be due to failure of the normal hormone responses to hypoglycaemia and to be reversible.

Pancreatic transplantation and pancreatic islet transplantation

Pancreatic transplantation, using the whole organ has been successfully practised at Guy's Hospital since 1996; 92 transplants have been performed with a cumulative patient survival of 85 per cent and insulin independence and pancreas survival of 74 per cent, making it one of the most successful programmes in Europe.

In 2005 the first UK islet cell transplant was performed at King's College Hospital. Three patients have been successfully injected with insulin-making pancreatic cells so far enabling one patient to be insulin independent and reducing insulin dependency by 50-85 per cent in the other patients. Researchers are now exploring the potential to perform remote islet cell isolation with the aim of providing islets for other UK centres to use in their transplant programmes.

While promising treatment, the availability of surgery is restricted by the shortage of donor pancreases from which to extract islet cells. King's researchers are working on growing pancreatic cells from stem cells to enable widespread availability of this life-changing surgery.

Can diabetes be prevented?

Type 1 diabetes is a chronic inflammatory autoimmune process that destroys islet beta cells, leading to insulin deficiency. There is currently no cure, and the disease is showing an alarming increase in children and adults. A greater understanding of the key checkpoints in the development of beta cell autoreactivity is allowing the rational development of immune intervention. Amongst the potentially critical checkpoints are firstly presentation of beta cell peptides to autoreactive T-cells, leading to their

Trials for a vaccine for Type 1 diabetes began in 2006 and brings hope of ending the burden of daily insulin injections for diabetics.

activation, and secondly failure(s) in the regulation of such peripheral T-cell autoreactivity. Research on patients with diabetes carried out in the Department of Immunobiology at King's has made important inroads in both areas. First, a series of beta cell peptides that activate autoreactive T-cells in an HLA- and disease-specific manner have been identified. Second, through analysis of regulatory pathways, two failures in peripheral regulation that could licence autoreactive T-cells to promote beta cell destruction have been identified. This knowledge is now being translated into therapeutic strategies, following the concept that beta cell-specific regulatory T-cells can be induced by simple injection of self peptides. This strategy has many notable successes in animal models, and is now being applied in man in a programme of clinical trials funded by the Diabetes Vaccine Development Centre. The first phase, starting in 2006, will examine both safety and the potential of such therapy to induce beta cell-specific regulatory T-cells. Because the approach generates a new immune response that may protect from disease, it has been dubbed a 'vaccine' for Type 1 diabetes. If successful, such vaccines could be tailor-made for individual patients, on the basis of their HLA genes and the beta cell targets that they recognize, making this the first 'designer vaccine' for human disease.

| Richard Bright FRS (1789-1858) | Thomas Addison (1795-1860) | George Budd FRS (1808-1882) | Sir William Gull FRS (1816-1890) | Sir George Johnson FRS (1818-1896) | John Laws Milton (1820-1898) | Frederic Akbar Mahomed (1849-1884) | Sir Nestor Tirard (1853-1928) | Charles Calnan (b 1917) |

Skin, kidney & liver studies: at the forefront of international excellence

Three separate specialties, studies of the skin, kidney and liver, all have an international reputation at this institution for their clinical excellence, research and postgraduate training. For decades they have been at the forefront of their fields with a reputation for innovation and for adopting the practice of taking the patients' diseases to the laboratory and returning to the bedside with improvements in understanding causes of disease, pathogenesis, and new treatments.

Skin science

The St John's Institute of Dermatology at King's is one of the world's premier dermatology institutes. Research scientists and clinicians work closely together to increase the understanding of normal and diseased skin. The importance of the Institute's research is reflected in the fact that 15 per cent of general practice consultations are for skin disease and at any one time, 20 per cent of the population suffers from skin disease requiring medical treatment.

The origins of dermatology research date back to the founding of the first skin clinic at Guy's in 1824 by Thomas Addison (1795-1860). Addison had a particular interest in skin diseases; in fact his description of his eponymous disease began its story

as a dermatological entity. Addison made several original observations on conditions including morphea and diabetic xanthomata. Sir William Gull (1816-1890) was his assistant and also made his own contributions.

A decade later St John's Hospital for Diseases of the Skin was founded by John Laws Milton (1820-1898) a surgeon who allegedly abused his position at St John's to run a lucrative practice treating the dubious condition of 'spermatorrhoea'. Despite this slur he made his clinical mark in dermatology with the first description of angioneurotic oedema.

The Institute of Dermatology in the University of London was closely associated with St John's and Charles Calnan (b 1917) was appointed to its first chair of dermatology in 1961. He was the first professor of

Victor Parsons
(1929-1995)

Roger Williams CBE
(b 1931)

Malcolm Greaves
(b 1933)

Stewart Cameron
(b 1934)

Alex Mowat (1935-1995)

Sir Cyril Chantler
(b 1939)

dermatology in London and only the second in the UK. Calnan and his colleagues developed a centre of clinical excellence with research programmes in the immunology of skin disease and the causes and photobiology of skin conditions precipitated by sunlight, the photodermatoses. His successor, Malcolm Greaves (b 1933) extended research to include dermatopharmacology, dermoatohistopathology and immunopathology, skin infections, contact and occupational diseases and genetics. This extensive development laid the foundation for the Institute's present work.

Skin complaints are one of the commonest causes for seeing a doctor today. Dermatology research at King's includes cancer, inflammatory and autoimmune disorders, genetic diseases and photobiology, and ranges from common diseases such as psoriasis, to rare blistering disorders.

Psoriasis affects more than one million people in the UK. Known for many years as partly inheritable, major and minor genes for its susceptibility have been identified at King's and their functional role examined. Researchers have shown that response to treatment with retinoids is variable and this too has been shown to have a genetic basis, helping towards the goal of therapy tailored to individual patients.

All skin diseases can be distressing, but few more so than blistering disorders. Blistering disorders such as Kindler's syndrome and lipoid proteinosis can prove fatal as the skin's natural barrier against infection is removed and they also predispose to skin cancer. King's researchers have identified that these two rare disorders have a genetic cause.

Kindler's syndrome is an autosomal recessive disorder causing not only blistering but skin fragility in childhood followed by premature ageing of the skin. The gene has been identified and its protein product, kindlin, has a vital role in cell adhesion and signalling.

Lipoid proteinosis has been mapped to a gene which normally controls the function of a glycoprotein (ECM1) which is one of the molecules which maintains the integrity of normal skin. Because the appearance of the skin in lipoid proteinosis is similar to that in the much commoner lichen sclerosus, an autoimmune disease, antibodies to ECM1 have been sought and found in 75 per cent of patients, confirming its autoimmune nature.

These techniques and their findings are not only relevant to diagnosis, including prenatal diagnosis, monitoring and possible treatment, but also have relevance to skin cancer, ageing and healing. Malignant diseases of the skin are an important part of dermatology research, and King's current research in this area is described on page 76.

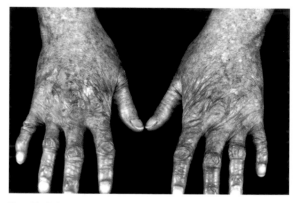

Above: Kindler's syndrome is characterised by blistering and skin fragility.

Left: John Laws Milton, founder of the St John's Hospital for Diseases of the Skin.

Nephrology

The history of renal disease at King's is dominated by the fundamental contribution of Richard Bright (1789-1858). However, while he is often referred to as the 'father of nephrology' for establishing the concept of diseases of the kidney (see page 20) he was not the first at this institution to make contributions in this field. Twenty years before Bright's notable observations, American-born physician Charles Wells (1757-1817) came to London and St Thomas' Hospital from North Carolina, having been a loyalist during the war of independence. His work on proteinuria in patients with dropsy and scarlet fever from 1805 to 1810 laid the foundations for Bright who wove together clinical observations, chemistry and pathology not only to begin the definition of renal diseases but also to lead the way to modern clinical thinking and methodology.

A succession of Guy's physicians made further contributions to study of the diseases, notably Frederic Akbar Mahomed (1849-1884) in renal and especially essential hypertension and Sir William Gull (1816-1890) who developed crucial ideas in vascular pathology and hypertension.

At King's College Hospital, Sir George Johnson (1818-1896) wrote prolifically on renal disease and hypertension, and Sir Nestor Tirard (1853-1928) was one of the earliest experts on renal disease in childhood. In the early years of the twentieth century Ernest Starling (1866-1927) developed his ideas of

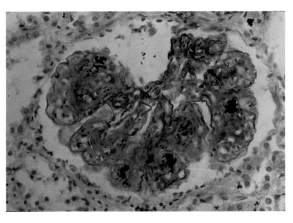

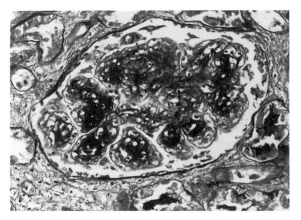

Two modern histological preparations from an original specimen of one of Richard Bright's patients, who presented with oedema and proteinuria. **Below** is a PAS stain showing the features of mesangiocapillary/membrano-proliferative glomerulonephritis (x280), and **above** the immunohistology shows deposition of the complement component C3 (x360).

capillary filtration and exchange, so important in renal function and oedema formation, before leaving Guy's for University College London.

As the techniques of renal biopsy and dialysis developed and the need to treat chronic renal failure became apparent, renal units were formed at Guy's in the 1960s by Stewart Cameron (b 1934), at King's College Hospital by Victor Parsons (1929-1995) and at St Thomas' by Norman Jones (b 1931). A unique opportunity arose at Guy's as a children's renal unit had been set up by Richard White (b 1930) allowing Cameron, and White's successor in 1973 Cyril Chantler (b 1939), and their colleagues to work at the interface of adult and paediatric nephrology, as well as in their own fields. Cameron's leadership and scholarship forged a renal unit with an international reputation for its linking of bedside observations with laboratory work and practice, and for its studies on the immunology, immunopathology and natural history of glomerulonephritis and the development of transplantation. The paediatric renal unit became the largest centre in the UK for children with renal failure and made contributions to preventing growth failure and long-term renal bone disease.

The unit at St Thomas', as well as developing dialysis and transplantation, played a unique role in the development of the European Registry of Dialysis and Transplantation, through the work of Anthony Wing (b 1933), which provided a matchless source of information on the practice and outcomes of renal

Starling's law

Ernest Starling observed in cardiac muscle that the force of contraction increased as the muscle was stretched in response to increased filling of the heart's chambers. It is essential that heart muscle responds in this way to stretching, otherwise circulation of blood would fail. This became known as 'Starling's law' and is fundamental to the understanding of the heart's function.

to clinical features of congestive heart failure. During this time he also carried out innovative studies on the electromotive force of the mammalian heart and with William Bayliss described the first successful attempts to record electrocardiograms in mammals.

Understanding blood flow

Starling's interests were broad and his work influenced many leading cardiologists of the time and continues to do so to this day. One of those influenced by Starling was Henry Barcroft (1904-1998). While at Cambridge Barcroft had developed a simple mechanical instrument called a stromuhr, for measuring the quantity of blood that flows per unit time through a blood vessel. When he moved to Starling's department at UCL he used the instrument and elegant surgical techniques developed by Starling to study the paradoxical increase in cardiac output after occlusion of the descending aorta. His painstaking work showed that the effect was a mechanical consequence of the redistribution of blood in the circulation and not due to an undiscovered circulatory reflex as had been previously supposed.

A few years later, during his time as Chair of Physiology at Queen's College Belfast, Barcroft became interested in the human peripheral circulation. He would stand for hours, together with research colleagues, in bins filled with water at core body temperature to test the effect of mechanical contraction of blood vessels on local blood flow. His

experiments showed that sustained muscle contraction at 20-30 per cent maximal strength almost completely arrested blood flow in the calf of the subject, whereas rhythmic contractions, such as whilst walking, increased blood flow.

Nervous control of circulation

Barcroft's most significant contribution to physiology was his observation that blood vessels in human skeletal muscle are innervated with sympathetic vasoconstrictor nerves. He showed that when ulnar and median nerves are blocked near the elbow, blood flow in the forearm is increased. He concluded that release of vasoconstrictor tone with deep nerve block was deep to skin and presumably in skeletal muscle. He went on to show that the vasodilatation seen in limbs in response to body heating is not controlled by the same vasoconstrictor fibres to muscles, but by release of vasoconstrictor tone in skin vessels only.

During World War II Barcroft collaborated with John McMichael and E P Sharpey-Schafer on the physiological effects of haemorrhage. Following the war, Barcroft was appointed Professor of Physiology at St Thomas' where he continued his studies of peripheral circulation with a particular interest in the vascular changes that take place after sympathectomy.

Blood flow and body temperature control

Another physiologist working at the same time as Starling and Barcroft was Ronald Thomson Grant (1892-1989). He was interested in how blood flow is altered in skin under different circumstances. Working at UCL, Grant published his first influential paper in 1924 which explained that the vascular changes that take place in skin following different types of injury result from a single mechanism that is similar to injecting histamine into the skin. In 1930 Grant published a paper that provided the first *in vivo* evidence of arteriovenous anastomoses – small blood vessels that interconnect an artery and a vein. Using an albino rabbit model he demonstrated the importance of these small vessels in regulating body heat and their sensitivity to sympathetic nerve stimulation.

In 1934 Grant became Director of the newly established MRC Clinical Research Unit at Guy's Hospital Medical School where he continued to work until the outbreak of World War II, when he was commissioned to work on trauma and shock (see pages 106-107).

He returned to the Guy's Unit in 1945 and continued his research until 1957. During this period he showed that there are variations in vascular responses in different parts of the human limb. A major difference is that, although body warming produces large increases in blood flow and skin temperature in hands and feet, it causes only a slight rise of forearm and leg blood flow. This is largely due to distribution of arteriovenous

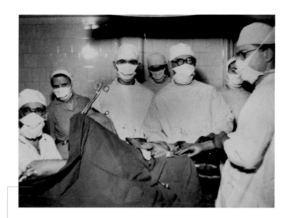

Russell (later Lord) Brock (centre right, wearing glasses) with the cardiac surgery team 1952. Brock was one of the foremost exponents and innovators of open heart surgery, developing in particular operations for diseased heart valves.

anastomoses, which are plentiful at the extremities but virtually absent in forearm and leg.

Grant also thought it interesting that blood vessels acquire a heightened reactivity to constrictor stimuli after denervation. He provided evidence for the presence of a sympathetic cholinergic nerve mechanism in the central artery of the rabbit's ear. His work suggested that after nerve section acetyl-choline release diminishes and this is, at least in part responsible for the heightened reactivity of the denervated vessel.

Clinical cardiology

Russell Claude Brock (1903-1980), who graduated from Guy's Hospital Medical School in 1928 was one of heart surgery's pioneers. Indeed, his interest in

heart surgery came at time when most established medical opinion believed that heart surgery should not be contemplated. Brock held consultant appointments at Guy's and Brompton Hospitals from 1936 to 1968 during which time his achievements gave him a widespread reputation.

During World War II Brock was thoracic surgeon and regional adviser in thoracic surgery to the Emergency Medical Service in the Guy's region. Following the war, thoracic surgery techniques and particularly open heart surgery developed rapidly. Brock played a major part in pioneering the surgical relief of mitral stenosis and other valvular lesions of the heart. He introduced the technique to correct pulmonary artery stenosis and right ventricular outflow tract obstruction in the beating heart. Brock's clinical experience demonstrated that even a severely underdeveloped pulmonary outflow tract could be restored to full growth by a successful direct operation.

Most open heart operations are conducted on a paralyzed heart – cardioplegia – and on coronary bypass. Cardioplegia obviously needs to be safe and reversible. One of the most notable achievements in cardiac surgery was the development of efficient cardioplegic solutions by the biochemist David Hearse at St Thomas' in the 1970s and 1980s.

Operating on the main blood vessels of the body – vascular surgery – was another major advance in treating disease of conditions due to partial or

Alfred Blalock (front centre) visited Guy's in 1947 and saved the lives of eight British children with the 'blue baby' heart condition.

Guy's and blue babies

Guy's surgeon Donald Ross performed the first total correction of Fallot's tetralogy (or so called 'blue baby syndrome') on a patient under one year of age in 1961. The baby was the youngest reported survivor of total correction of Fallot's by open heart surgery. Now 45, he is also the longest survivor in the world. Ross went on to work at the Brompton Hospital where he performed the UK's first heart transplant in 1968. The very first 'blue baby' operation at Guy's was in 1947 by world-famous American heart surgeon Alfred Blalock of Johns Hopkins Medical School. Blalock was visiting the medical school as part of a newly established exchange programme between Johns Hopkins and Guy's Medical School. This exchange programme continues to run to this day.

complete obstruction of arteries, or less commonly veins. Sir Norman Browse (b 1931), Professor of Surgery at St Thomas', and President of the Royal College of Surgeons from 1992-1995, contributed to this field by popularizing carotid endarterectomy to relieve or prevent cerebral ischaemia.

Abnormal rhythms of the heart – cardiac arrhythmias – are a common cause of illness and death, and although more common in the elderly can also affect children and young adults. The now routine use of cardiac pacemakers currently used for 25,000 patients per annum has transformed the prognosis for many of these patients. Edgar Sowton (1930-1994) was an unusual medical student, gaining simultaneous degrees in physics and medicine at Cambridge. He turned this basic knowledge to good effect in his internationally recognized achievement on the

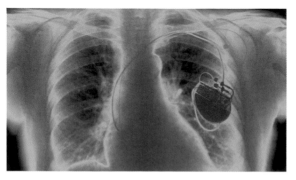

A cardiac pacemaker in place. Pacemakers have transformed the lives of thousands of patients with cardiac arrhythmis.

Stimulating the heart

Edgar Sowton's career at the Karolinska in Stockholm, the National Heart Hospital in London and then at Guy's, was devoted to the new clinical science of electrical stimulation of the heart. In the 1960s he became one of the world's pioneers in the development of pacemakers.

He was also one of the first people in the UK to perform coronary angioplasty. The biannual King's Edgar Sowton Memorial Lecture was established in his memory after his death in 1994.

development of cardiac pacemakers and the study of cardiac arrhythmias. He started this work at the Institute of Cardiology, London, and continued it on his appointment to Guy's.

Biopsy of the heart posed a very difficult problem because of its relative inaccessibility and the risk of bleeding until the development by Peter Richardson at King's College Hospital of endomyocardial biopsy in the 1970s. This technique is now used worldwide, with the instrument still termed the 'King's bioptome'.

Paediatric cardiology has been a strength at Guy's since its inception. Under the guidance of Michael Tynan (b 1934) the Guy's team grew an international reputation for its management of congenital heart disease. Surgical and invasive imaging techniques for correcting congenital abnormalities as well as innovations in diagnostic ultrasound all had an important impact on the specialty. These techniques were also developed for use *in utero*, contributing to the rise of the new discipline of fetal cardiology.

Current research follows in the traditions of the pioneering cardiac and vascular physiology dating back to the days of Starling as well as applied work on the diagnosis and treatment of coronary artery disease and heart failure.

Cardiac muscle

Interest in cardiac muscle physiology has been strong at King's for several decades, notably within the MRC Muscle Group (see page 23) which has focused on

Beta blockers for heart disease
Sir James Black (b 1924), Emeritus Professor of Analytical Pharmacology at King's, received the Nobel Prize for Physiology or Medicine in 1988 for the development of beta-blockers, used for the treatment of coronary heart disease, high blood pressure and heart failure and anti-ulcer histamine receptor blocking drugs, including the best-selling Tagamet. Sir James is credited with introducing analytical pharmacology as a new way of thinking to the process of drug development (see pages 63-66).

fundamental mechanisms of muscle contraction using state-of-the-art biophysical techniques. Recent work has shown that the cellular basis of Starling's law actually lies at the level of the myofilaments, and that regulation of cardiac muscle is modulated by factors such as endothelial cell-derived nitric oxide, and novel protein kinases.

A fundamentally new view of cardiac muscle function has arisen from the discovery that proteins within the muscle sarcomeres are not only important as structural components and in contraction but also serve major cell signalling functions that impact on cardiac growth and development of disease. For example, a giant protein known as titin which spans the entire sarcomere contains domains that are capable of sensing mechanical forces applied to the muscle and then initiating signalling cascades that modulate muscle protein synthesis and atrophy or hypertrophy. This pathway is implicated in certain cardio-myopathies and may provide a new therapeutic target.

Signalling

Cellular signalling in cardiovascular pathologies is a major research theme with specific focus on the role of redox signalling pathways that are regulated by the local production of small amounts of oxygen radicals and on protein kinase pathways involved in cardiac adaptive responses to myocardial ischaemia. Redox-regulated pathways are implicated in the pathophysiology of cardiac hypertrophy, heart

It is estimated that around 200 million people across the world have had their sight saved thanks to Ridley's vision and determination, including former South African president Nelson Mandela and the late Queen Mother. In the 1980s Ridley himself had both lenses replaced. 'I am the only man to have invented his own operation' Ridley said. It was fitting that the surgery was performed at St Thomas', the hospital where he had himself pioneered intraocular lens replacement surgery.

William Briggs   William Cheselden   William Bowman

Early pioneers of ophthalmology

Contributions to ophthalmology can be traced back at this institution to the 1600s when St Thomas' physician William Briggs (1642-1704) named the optic papilla and the retinal nerve fibres in his book *Ophthalmographia* published in 1676.
William Cheselden (1688-1752) famous anatomist and surgeon, made great advances in eye surgery the following century when he described his operation of iridectomy for the treatment of blindness by incising the iris and making an artificial pupil. In 1728 he reported that he restored the sight of a boy of 13 who had been born blind, by performing this procedure.
Cheselden was also a sought-after surgeon for the removal of cataracts.
Ophthalmology as a distinct discipline owes much to William Bowman (1816-1892), a leading ophthalmic surgeon and anatomist at King's College Hospital. Through use of microscopes, he described and named several structures including Bowman's membrane in the cornea, and the minute structure of the ciliary muscle and the iris. He also surgically removed cataracts by a suction technique. In 1880 he was elected the first president of the Ophthalmological Society having been instrumental in its founding.

Florence Nightgale OM
(1820-1910)

Frederick Newland Pedley
(1859-1944)

William Kelsey Fry
(1889-1963)

Ronald Thomson Grant
OBE FRS (1892-1989)

Henry Barcroft FRS
(1904-1998)

Lord Butterfield OBE
(1920-2000)

War & medicine

War creates huge medical problems, but also stimulates new treatments.

Notable contributions to this area from people associated with King's and its constituent institutions include Florence Nightingale's transformation of military hospitals; wartime dental surgery by Frederick Newland Pedley and Sir William Kelsey Fry; research on war injuries by doctors Ronald Grant, Henry Barcroft and John Butterfield and the achievements of the current King's Centre for Military Health Research.

Lessons from the Crimean War

Florence Nightingale's work in the Crimea as 'the lady of the lamp' is legendary and it was as a tribute to her achievements there that a public subscription was launched in 1855 which established the fund that enabled Nightingale (1820-1910) to found the world's first professional nursing school at St Thomas' Hospital in 1860, now incorporated into the King's College Florence Nightingale School of Nursing & Midwifery.

The Crimean War, which began in 1854, ranged Britain, France and Turkey against Russia. Although the Russians were defeated at the battle of the Alma River in 1854, there were extensive British casualties and *The Times* strongly criticised the British medical facilities. In response, Nightingale was asked by the Secretary for War to oversee the introduction of nurses to military hospitals in the war zone. She arrived in Scutari (near Istanbul), with 38 nurses in 1854 as 'Superintendent of the Female Nursing Establishment of the English General Hospitals in Turkey' and set about reforming the hospital system – often in opposition to the military authorities.

She found soldiers lying on bare floors surrounded by vermin, unhygienic operations and diseases such as cholera and typhus rife in the hospitals. Injured soldiers were seven times more likely to die from disease in hospital than on the battlefield. Nightingale collected data and organised a record keeping system, using her statistics to improve city and military hospitals. Through the establishment of a fresh water supply and measures to improve hygiene, as well as using her own funds to buy fruit, vegetables and standard hospital equipment, the mortality rate dropped significantly.

Frederick Newland Pedley, founder of the Guy's Dental School, was the first dental surgeon to accompany British troops in a war zone, during the Boer War.

The work of maxillo-facial surgeon William Kelsey Fry was recorded in 'before-and-after' pastel drawings by the surgeon and artist Henry Tonks.

Pastel before

Pastel after

On her return to London in August 1856, Nightingale pressed for sanitary reform in all military hospitals and was instrumental in bringing about the establishment of the Royal Commission on the Health of the Army in 1858. Despite crippling illness (perhaps brucellosis contracted in the Crimea), she continued to campaign on behalf of military health and on behalf of public health in India, as well as establishing and overseeing the progress of the Nightingale School of Nursing. She advised on army medical care in Canada and was a consultant to the United States Government on army health during the American Civil War. She became the first woman to receive the Order of Merit from Edward VII in 1907.

Boer War and First World War

Major contributions to the health of Service personnel in these two wars were made by two famous Guy's dentists. The founder (in 1888) of the Guy's Dental School, Frederick Newland Pedley (1859-1944), was the first dental surgeon ever to accompany British troops in a war zone. During the Boer War (1899-1902), the incidence of pyorrhoea and dental sepsis was so high that of the 208,000 men in the field, no less than 7,000 were admitted to hospital for dental reasons, and 2,500 of these were invalided home. In February 1900 Newland Pedley went out at his own expense for six months to serve as Honorary Dental Surgeon.

Above Florence Nightingale in the Military Hospital at Scutari, lithograph by J A Benwell, 1855.

Below The Battle of Inkerman, whose casualties Florence Nightingale tended in the Crimea in 1854.

Colonel (later Sir) William Kelsey Fry (1889-1963), a pioneer of maxillo-facial surgery, trained at Guy's and had just been appointed a lecturer at the Dental School when he joined the Royal Army Medical Corps at the outbreak of the First World War. With the New Zealand plastic surgeon Harold Gillies (later Sir Harold), he revolutionised the treatment and management of jaw and facial injuries from explosive shells and high velocity missiles, developing effective treatment principles and techniques that are still relevant today. Fry returned to Guy's after the war and became one of the leading oral surgeons in the country, developing new treatment techniques for patients with cleft palates and other facial deformities.

Second World War

Before the Second World War the pathophysiology of shock due to trauma was hardly understood and blood transfusion was not yet a widely practised treatment. The injuries in civilians caused by bombing and those of service personnel stimulated research on haemorrhage and its physiological consequences. Henry Barcroft (1904-1998), Professor of Physiology at St Thomas' Hospital from 1948, was interested in the nervous and humoral control of blood vessels and had studied the effects of haemorrhage in volunteers at the Royal Postgraduate Medical School (see page 96). More immediate work was carried out by Ronald Grant and Basil Reeve.

Ronald Grant (1892-1989), joined Guy's Hospital Medical School in 1934 as Director of the newly-established Clinical Research Unit of the Medical Research Council (MRC), researching the physiology and pathology of the smaller blood vessels. Their work on the condition of 'traumatic shock' or 'wound shock' began during the heavy air raids in London. When large-scale air-raids on London ceased, the Unit was transferred to the Royal Victoria Infirmary in Newcastle upon Tyne where Grant and Reeve continued their research on patients injured in industrial and road accidents. At the end of 1943 Grant persuaded the MRC to move his researches to a battle zone and the First Traumatic Shock Research Unit was formed in the Royal Army Medical Corps to study injuries on the Italian battlefield around Monte Cassino in 1944-45.

Grant and Reeve recognized that haemorrhage was a major factor in wound shock. They recommended that, if transfusions were received early enough after injury, patients with the most massive injuries and continuing haemorrhage could be kept alive by transfusion, and that blood volume measurements were most helpful in guiding the amount of blood required for transfusion. They also drew attention to the serious disturbances of water and electrolyte balance that can follow abdominal injuries. Grant was mentioned in despatches and received the OBE in 1945, when he returned to Guy's to continue his researches.

Queen Elizabeth and King George VI inspect bomb damage at St Thomas', Summer 1940.

Cold War

Before he began his important work on diabetes and insulin (see page 87) John Butterfield (1920-2000), was appointed to the staff of the Medical Research Council in 1946 and spent four years as a major with the Royal Army Medical Corps estimating the effects which nuclear explosions would have on the skin. Working in sheds made of lead six inches thick at Byfleet, in Surrey, he and a group of colleagues exposed their arms to intensely hot lamps. 'We used a shutter affair rather like a massive toaster', Butterfield

A philosophical advantage

Ronald Grant and Basil Reeve had an unusual research assistant. The philosopher Ludwig Wittgenstein (1889-1951) worked as a porter at Guy's Hospital from 1941 and then with Ronald Grant's team at Newcastle from 1943 to 1944 as a laboratory assistant. Wittgenstein, who had become a naturalised British citizen in 1939, was at this stage Professor of Philosophy at Cambridge, working on mathematics and logic, but felt that he could not grapple with, or teach, philosophy 'while the world was falling apart', as he put it. Grant wrote of Wittgenstein's contribution to their work: 'He has a keenly critical mind and in discussions of medical and physiological problems has proved a most helpful and stimulating colleague. He has undertaken observations on respiratory variations of blood pressure in man, devising his own experiments and apparatus. The results of his work so far are at variance with commonly accepted views and of considerable interest'. It was Wittgenstein who suggested to Grant that wound sizes might be described in terms of the volume of tissue damaged, using the hand or fist as a unit of measurement, and this made a significant contribution to Grant's work on measuring wounds and blood-loss.

Remembering Keats

The John Keats Memorial Lecture is held every two years on the anniversary of Keats's death (23rd February 1821). It was founded jointly by the Royal College of Surgeons of England, the Worshipful Society of Apothecaries and Guy's Hospital in memory of Keats. The 2005 lecture was given by Poet Laureate and Keats biographer Andrew Motion.

Doodle from Keats's medical notebook.

As might be expected, Keats found this work agonising. His 'Ode to a Nightingale' (1819), for example, evokes

> The weariness, the fever and the fret
> Here, where men sit and hear each other groan;
> Where palsy shakes a few, sad, last gray hairs,
> Where youth grows pale, and spectre-thin, and dies;

while in *Endymion* (1818) Keats uses the unusual simile 'remorseless as an Infant's bier' to describe a transformation scene, in which 'shrieks, yells, and groans of torture-pilgrimage' accompany the bloating of men's bodies as they are changed into animals.

It was while he was at Guy's that Keats first began to write poetry, and also during this time that he became associated with radical thinkers and writers. By late 1816 he had decided to try to make his living as a poet rather than an apothecary or surgeon, and he left his medical studies never to return. Keats's time at Guy's is commemorated by a memorial lecture held every two years at the anniversary of his death.

Medicine and the arts as a discipline

Professor Green's polymath status and attitudes anticipate the way in which the links between medicine and the arts have grown and strengthened at King's, especially in the last few decades. In 1978 King's established a Centre of Medical Law & Ethics, the first of its kind in the UK. It is a leader in

promoting research, discussion and training in this area. In 2000 the College's 'Medicine & Humanity' debates in Southwark Cathedral explored medicine and morality at the millennium, with speakers including Professors Robert Winston and Kay

Bust of Joseph Henry Green, first professor of medicine at King's College London, Kantian philosopher and friend of Samuel Taylor Coleridge.

Redfield Jamison and the future Archbishop of Canterbury, Dr Rowan Williams. These debates were published by the King's Fund in 2001.

In 2001 the College appointed the UK's first Professor in Medicine & the Arts. Established with a grant of £2 million from the D'Oyly Carte Charitable Trust, this unique chair stimulates teaching and research in the creative, literary and performing arts and their relationship with medicine in its broadest sense. Professor Brian Hurwitz's own interests encompass clinical medicine, ethics, law, medical history, and the role of narrative thinking in medical practice.

In 2005 Professor Hurwitz organised a lecture series exploring the dialogue between the disciplines of literature and medicine, with lectures given by international scholars of clinical medicine and literary studies on subjects including narrative and medicine, and representations of childhood in nineteenth-century fiction and psychiatry.

A multi-faculty tradition

As a multi-faculty institution, King's offers some of the most diverse study options of any UK medical school. Of its 900 special study module (SSM) titles, students can choose from a range of subjects outside medicine including law, modern languages, music, maths and philosophy. Medical students are also able to intercalate bachelors' degrees in philosophy, clinical ethics and law. King's has the only UK medical school in which undergraduates can study for the Diploma in Medical History of the Society of Apothecaries as part of their SSMs.

King's also offers some unique subjects. In 2004 King's launched its Music and Medicine SSM. The module explores current understanding of how the brain perceives, produces and appreciates music; psychological and physiological responses to music and musical psychotherapy; the psychology of the musician, the composer and the performer, and the effect of health on musical composition. Topics covered by students have included 'Sex, drugs and Schubert'; 'Musical Savants' and the theme of tuberculosis in music, with 'case notes' on Violetta in Verdi's *La Traviata* and Mimi in Puccini's *La Bohème*.

Bodyworks: Images of the Body in Western Art is an anatomy SSM which explores thematic imagery and

Scene from Offenbach's *Tales of Hoffman* (Royal Opera House). King's offers the only Special Study Module in Music and Medicine in the UK. The module recently included a lecture sponsored by English National Opera on the representation of doctors and disease in opera.

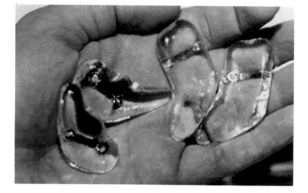

concepts involved in the representation of the body in art, and draws parallels with aspects of medical practice. Contributions to the course by two practising artists include exhibitions at the Guy's Campus: 'Images of Consciousness' by Veronica Vossen and 'The Valley of Dry Bones' by Olivia Downey.

In 2005 King's launched the UK's first MA in Literature & Medicine. This complements the MSc in the Philosophy of Mental Disorder, run jointly between the Department of Philosophy and the Institute of Psychiatry.

Increasing perceptions of disease

A collaboration in 2003 between medicine and art at King's, funded by a Wellcome Trust People Award and a SciArt Award, has led to the improvement of facial reconstruction surgery for accident victims. During a period as Artist in Residence in Oral & Maxillofacial Surgery, ceramicist Paddy Hartley worked with King's material scientists on the sculpting of tailor-made 'bioactive glass' implants. This material opens within hours of implantation and allows tissue to grow into it, and has helped to rectify broken cheekbones and saved the sight of patients whose optic nerve would be damaged by collapsed bone.

In 2002 a collaboration between visual artist Deborah Padfield, Dr Charles Pither, Pain Specialist at St Thomas' Hospital, and Professor Hurwitz produced an exhibition and a book which united the metaphorical testimonies of patients suffering from chronic pain and abstract photography to produce an alternative visual language to communicate pain. *Perceptions of Pain* was funded by a Wellcome Trust SciArt award and by the Guy's and St Thomas' Charity. The images demonstrate the role which art can play in projecting interior subjective experience on to external shareable surfaces, and evaluation of the use of 64 of the images, piloted as a booklet in 20 NHS pain clinics, indicates that images of pain can facilitate communication between pain sufferers and doctors.

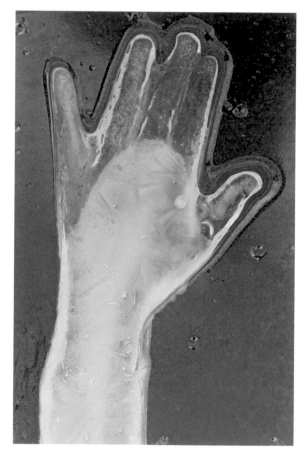

Notable names

Notable people, who have died or retired, connected with this institution are listed here. They are noted for their major contributions to biomedicine which have impacted on the understanding of disease and improving the treatment of illness. For reasons of space, not all are mentioned in more detail in this edition of this book.

THOMAS ADDISON (1795-1860)
Alumnus and lecturer in *materia medica* and practice of medicine, Guy's; important work on skin and respiratory diseases; described Addisonian anaemia and Addison's disease (1855), initiating science of endocrinology; introduced scientific method to clinical medicine; *p15, 17-20, 89.*

SIR HEDLEY ATKINS (1905-1983)
Guy's alumnus; first Professor of Surgery at Guy's (1961); carried out comparative trials of treatments for breast cancer; pioneered combined therapies and recognised the influence of hormones on prognosis; *p73-74.*

BENJAMIN BABINGTON FRS (1794-1866)
Alumnus and physician, Guy's; linguist and oriental scholar; invented laryngoscope; founder of the Epidemiological Society; son of William Babington.

WILLIAM BABINGTON FRS (1756-1833)
Alumnus and physician, Guy's; lectured on chemistry and promoted development of mineralogy and the Geological Society.

PETER BAKER FRS (1939-1987)
Professor of Physiology, King's; studied ion fluxes across cell membranes of peripheral nerves; *p38.*

HENRY BARCROFT FRS (1904-1998)
Professor of Physiology, St Thomas'; studied the effects of haemorrhage; *p96, 106.*

LIONEL SMITH BEALE FRS (1828-1906)
Professor of Physiology and later Medicine at King's; published influential work, *The Microscope and its Application to Clinical Medicine* (1854); *p15.*

ARNOLD BECKETT OBE (b 1920)
Professor of Pharmaceutical Chemistry, Chelsea College; Emeritus Professor of Pharmacology, King's; pioneered tests for detecting drug abuse in sport; *p63-65.*

ARNOLD BENDER (1918-1999)
Professor of Nutrition and Dietetics, Queen Elizabeth College; made links with food science and nutrition and formulated with Derek Miller, the Bender-Miller Net Protein Utilisation method of assaying the nutritive value of proteins; *p47.*

SIR JAMES BLACK OM FRS (b 1924)
Emeritus Professor of Analytical Pharmacology at King's; discovered beta-blockers, notably propanolol, and anti-ulcer drug cimetidine; awarded Nobel Prize for Physiology or Medicine 1988; *p11, 63-64, 65, 99.*

JAMES BLUNDELL (1790-1878)
Alumnus Guy's and St Thomas'; lecturer in midwifery and physiology at Guy's; experimented with and invented instruments for blood transfusion; *p8, 51-52, 53.*

PROFESSOR GUSTAV BORN FRS (b 1921)
Emeritus Professor of Pharmacology, King's; contributions to thrombosis and coagulation of blood.

SIR WILLIAM BOWMAN FRS (1816-1892)
Ophthalmologist and anatomist at King's College London and King's College Hospital; pioneer in use of microscopes; studied muscle, kidneys, eye and liver; Bowman's capsule (kidney), Bowman's gland (olfactory mucosa) and Bowman's membrane (cornea) named after him; first president of the Ophthalmological Society; *p15, 101, 104.*

JOHN BRAXTON HICKS (1823-1897)
Obstetrician, Guy's; first to describe podalic version of the fetus and those contractions in pregnancy not leading to childbirth which are known by his name; *p51, 53.*

WILLIAM BRIGGS (1642-1704)
Physician and oculist, St Thomas'; published an anatomy of the eye, *Ophthalmographia* (1676) naming the optic papilla and retinal nerve fibres; 'Theory of vision' was translated and acknowledged by Newton; *p104.*

RICHARD BRIGHT FRS (1789-1858)
Alumnus, Guy's and St Thomas'; physician and charismatic lecturer at Guy's from 1820; with Addison, wrote *Elements of the Practice of Medicine* (1839), including important description of acute appendicitis; described symptoms and signs of impaired renal function, providing the early clinico-pathological classification of nephritis, called Bright's disease; introduced scientific method to clinical medicine; *p15, 17-20, 87, 91.*

JOHN BRISTOWE FRS (1827-1895)
Alumnus, King's College London and St Thomas'; physician and lecturer, St Thomas'; best-known for public health work, with reports on the rag trade and the role of phosphorus in jaw necrosis among match workers; in 1863, conducted substantial research on the hospitals of the United Kingdom to resolve a debate between Sir John Simon and Florence Nightingale about the site for the new St Thomas' Hospital.

LORD BROCK (RUSSELL CLAUDE BROCK) (1903-1980)
Alumnus and surgeon, Guy's; cardiovascular and thoracic specialist; pioneered the surgical relief of mitral stenosis; introduced a technique to correct pulmonary artery stenosis and right ventricular outflow tract obstruction; *p95, 97.*

SIR NORMAN BROWSE (b 1931)
Professor of Vascular Surgery, St Thomas'; President of the Royal College of Surgeons England (1992-1995); developed and popularised vascular surgery techniques; *p98*.

GEORGE BUDD FRS (1808-1882)
Carried out research on cholera and scurvy while physician to the Dreadnought Seaman's Hospital and became expert on diseases of the stomach and liver, described Budd-Chiari syndrome; elected Professor of Medicine, King's College London in 1840; *p93*.

LORD BUTTERFIELD (JOHN BUTTERFIELD) OBE (1920-2000)
Studied flash burns and the effects of the atomic bomb; Professor of Experimental Medicine at Guy's (1958); developed innovative diabetes treatments; with Harry Keen, instigated the Bedford Population Study of blood sugar, diabetes and coronary heart disease; *p87, 107-108*.

CHARLES CALNAN (b 1917)
Dermatologist; appointed first Professor of Dermatology at the Institute of Dermatology, University of London; research on the immunology of skin disease and photodermatoses; *p89-90*.

IAN CAMERON CBE (b 1936)
St Thomas' alumnus; Professor of Medicine, UMDS; Dean, St Thomas' 1986-1989; Principal UMDS 1989-1992; work on central and peripheral nervous control of breathing and regulation of pulmonary circulation; *p82*.

STEWART CAMERON (b 1934)
Nephrologist; founded Renal Unit at Guy's; Professor of Renal Medicine at Guy's; contributions to glomerular disease and renal transplantation; *p91*.

SIR CYRIL CHANTLER (b 1939)
Principal UMDS 1992-1998; Vice-Principal, King's College London 1998-2000; Pro-Vice Chancellor, University of London 1997-2000; developed paediatric nephrology and renal transplantation; *p58, 91*.

WILLIAM CHESELDEN FRS (1688-1752)
Alumnus and surgeon, St Thomas'; published *The Anatomy of the Human Body* (1713), a standard text for 100 years and *Osteographia* (1733) which provided first full description of human bone structure; developed new surgical techniques, especially for bladder stone extraction and eye surgery; made first artificial pupil through iridectomy; *p12, 14, 101, 104*.

SIR WILLIAM WATSON CHEYNE FRS (1852-1932)
Bacteriologist and surgeon; accompanied Lister to King's College Hospital (1877); later appointed Professor of Principles and Practice of Surgery and Professor of Clinical Surgery; promoted Lister's methods in writing and lectures; helped establish the science of bacteriology; *p69*.

TIMOTHY CLARK (b 1935)
Guy's alumnus; Professor of Thoracic Medicine, UMDS; Dean, Guy's 1986-1989; Principal, UMDS 1989-1992; emphasised the importance of the 'morning dip' in respiratory function; *p81*.

HENRY CLINE FRS (1750-1827)
Alumnus and surgeon, St Thomas'; published *On the Form of Animals* (1805).

EDWARD COCK (1805-1892)
Surgeon at Guy's; editor of *Guy's Hospital Reports*; first English surgeon to succeed in pharyngotomy; described Cock's procedure (opening the urethra through the perineum) in 1866.

SIR ASTLEY PASTON COOPER FRS (1768-1841)
Innovative surgeon and respected teacher of surgery and anatomy; advocate of dissection; first to operate on major blood vessels and to describe Cooper's ligaments of the breast and Cooper's pubic ligament; *p9, 11-15*.

JAMES HENRY CYRIAX (1904-1985)
Orthopaedic physician; alumnus and medical officer, St Thomas'; work on tennis elbow, carpal tunnel syndrome, the spine and referred pain; founded the Society of Orthopaedic Medicine (1979) to educate doctors and raise the professional status of physiotherapists; his *Textbook of Orthopaedic Medicine* went into 10 editions.

JAMES FREDERIC DANIELLI FRS (1911-1984)
Elected Professor of Zoology at King's College London (1949); first generally accepted model of the cell membrane (1935); work on quantitative study of cellular chemistry and anti-cancer drugs; campaigned for the preservation of the DNA of endangered species; his work on the transplantation of nuclei between amoebae stimulated research on the function of the nucleus and the mechanisms of developmental biology; *p22*.

SIR RICHARD DOLL FRS (1912-2005)
Alumnus of St Thomas'; led research study that proved link between lung cancer and smoking; awarded UN prize for outstanding research into the causes and control of cancer and Bisset Hawkins medal of the Royal College of Physicians for contributions to preventative medicine; *p74*.

IAN DONALD CBE (1910-1987)
Reader at St Thomas' Hospital, later at Hammersmith Hospital and University of Glasgow; main research interest in respiratory problems of the newborn; p84.

LEONARD STANLEY DUDGEON (1876-1938)
Pathologist and pioneer of cytology; alumnus of, and later head of Louis Jenner Clinical Laboratory at St Thomas'; investigated infectious disease among troops in the First World War; developed methods of diagnosing cancer using smears of bodily fluids and tumours; many papers on tropical disease, bacteriology and immunity; *p73*.

JOHN ELLIOTSON FRS (1791-1868)
Physician, St Thomas' (1817-1834); innovator in treatment of many conditions: first to use iodine in the treatment of goitre and first to link hay fever to atmospheric conditions; wrote on the medicinal properties of prussic acid, opium and creosote; credited with the introduction of the stethoscope to England; later involved with phrenology and mesmerism.

MURRAY FALCONER (1910-1977)
Neurosurgeon; in 1942 set up neurosurgical unit at the Maudsley (later the Guy's, Maudsley and King's College Hospital unit); pioneered surgical treatment for drug-resistant temporal lobe epilepsy, performing over 300 lobotomies; *p37*.

SIR WILLIAM FERGUSSON FRS (1808-1877)
Surgeon; Professor of Surgery King's College London; introduced principle of conservative surgery; revived the operation for cleft palate; devised many instruments still in use today including bone forceps and vaginal speculum.

SIR DAVID FERRIER FRS (1843-1928)
Neurologist; first chair of neuropathology at King's College London (1889); used electrical excitation of the brain to prove the localization of cerebral functions, making brain surgery feasible; co-founder of the journal *Brain* in 1878; *The Functions of the Brain* (1876) was translated into several languages; *p35-36*.

JOHN COOPER FORSTER (1823-1886)
Surgeon, Guy's (1841-1880); performed first gastrostomy in England in 1858 on a cancer of oesophagus; published *The Surgical Diseases of Children* (1860) based on his experience as surgeon to the Royal Hospital for Women and Children.

ROSALIND FRANKLIN (1920-1958)
Crystallographer; in 1951 established an X-ray diffraction laboratory at King's College London to study the structure of DNA; distinguished two forms of DNA and produced X-ray images of helical structure of DNA; *p10, 25-28*.

SIR ALFRED BARING GARROD FRS (1819-1907)
Physician, appointed Professor of *Materia Medica* and Therapeutics at King's College Hospital in 1863; undertook chemical pathological investigations of disease; discovered the increased levels of uric acid in the blood in gout (1848); distinguished rheumatoid arthritis from gout; coined the phrase 'rheumatoid arthritis'; *p33-34*.

SIR DAVID GOLDBERG (b 1934)
Head of the Department of Psychiatry 1993-1999; understanding of mental health services; assessment of common health disorders; *p61*.

PETER GORER FRS (1907-1961)
Alumnus, Guy's; primarily responsible for the application of genetic principles to immunology, making important contributions to the study of organ and tissue graft rejection, tumour immunity, and the genetics of immune responsiveness; discovered murine H-2; *p31-35, 74*.

RAYMOND GOSLING (b 1926)
Pioneered X-ray diffraction research at King's; worked with Wilkins (producing first crystalline diffraction photographs) and Franklin (to perfect technique of x-ray diffraction photography of DNA); Emeritus Professor in Physics Applied to Medicine; *p26-27, 30*.

RONALD THOMSON GRANT OBE FRS (1892-1989)
Director of Guy's Clinical Research Unit from 1934; studied the effects of haemorrhage on circulation; *p97, 106-107*.

MALCOLM GREAVES (b 1933)
Second Professor of Dermatology at the Institute of Dermatology; extended the Institute's research to include dermatopharmacology, dermatohistopathology and immunopathology; skin infections; occupational disease and genetics; *p90*.

JOSEPH HENRY GREEN FRS (1791-1863)
Alumnus and surgeon, St Thomas'; first Professor of Surgery at King's College London (1830); proposed a unified approach to surgical education, advancing 'surgery from a mechanical art to the rank of a liberal profession'; *p109, 110, 111*.

EDWARD HEADLAM GREENHOW FRS (1814-1888)
Epidemiologist; lecturer on public health at St Thomas' (1856).

SIR WILLIAM WITHEY GULL FRS (1816-1890)
Alumnus, later physician and governor, Guy's; *p48, 89, 91*.

THOMAS GUY (1644-1724)
Bookseller; governor of St Thomas' Hospital and founder of Guy's Hospital; *p8, 77, 78*.

JOHN HAIGHTON FRS (1755-1823)
Alumnus, later lecturer, St Thomas'; developed designs for obstetric forceps; *p51, 53*.

JEAN HANSON FRS (1919-1973)
Founder member of biophysics research unit at King's College London (1948); isolated myofibrils to allow *in vitro* investigation; first to describe double sliding filament mechanism of muscle contraction; Professor of Biology at King's College London (1966); *p21, 22*.

WILLIAM HALLIBURTON FRS (1860-1931)
Professor of Physiology at King's College London (1890-1923); first honorary member of the Biochemical Society (1923); early work on separation of proteins.

FREDERICK HEAF (1894-1973)
Alumnus, St Thomas'; Medical Officer in charge of anti-tuberculosis service for London; as Professor of Tuberculosis at the University of Wales, devised and validated the standard puncture 'Heaf test' for detecting tuberculosis; *p70*.

JOHN HILTON FRS (1805-1878)
Surgeon and anatomist; alumnus, Guy's; first to reduce obturator hernia by abdominal section; one of first to practice lumbar colostomy; numerous eponyms in anatomy including Hilton's law; Hilton's line; Hilton's muscle; Hilton's pit; *p15*.

JAMES HINTON (1822-1875)
First aural surgeon at Guy's (1863); first in Britain to perform a mastoid operation; *The Questions of Aural Surgery* (1874), describes 'glue ear' and the attempt to insert ventilation tubes (grommets).

THOMAS HODGKIN (1798-1866)
Guy's alumnus; first curator of the Anatomy Museum at Guy's, now The Gordon Museum; first systematic lectures on pathology in UK; first descriptions of several disorders, including his eponymous disease; introduced scientific method to clinical medicine; *p15, 17-20, 49, 73*.

WALTER HOLLAND CBE (b 1929)
Alumnus and Professor of Clinical Epidemiology and Social Medicine, St Thomas'; epidemiology of chronic respiratory disease, blood pressure and the application of epidemiologic principles to health services research; *p50*.

SIR FREDERICK GOWLAND HOPKINS OM FRS (1861-1947)
Guy's alumnus; Awarded 1929 Nobel Prize for Physiology or Medicine for research on vitamins and beriberi; taught physiology and toxicology at Guy's Hospital (1894-1898); *p46*.

PHILIP HUGH-JONES (b 1914)
Respiratory physician; developed lung function tests and a simple standard exercise test (King's College Hospital); *p81-82*.

MICHAEL HUTT (1922-2000)
Professor of Geographical Pathology, St Thomas'; work in East Africa on epidemiology and environmental risk factors for Burkitt's lymphoma and Kaposi's sarcoma; established one of the first cancer registers; *p74*.

SIR GEORGE JOHNSON FRS (1818-1896)
Member of the senate of London University, Professor of *Materia Medica*, physician and Professor of Clinical Medicine at King's College Hospital; wrote on renal disease and hypertension; *p91*.

NORMAN JONES (b 1931)
Nephrologist; founded renal unit at St Thomas'; *p91*.

HARRY KEEN CBE (b 1925)
Professor of Metabolic Medicine; developed continuous subcutaneous insulin infusion; conducted the Bedford Population Study with John Butterfield and the Guy's team; first description of microalbuminuria; *p86, 87*.

ROBERT DANIEL LAWRENCE (1892-1968)
Physician to the Department of Diabetes, King's College Hospital (1932); tested insulin and the effects of diet and exercise; established the Diabetic Association; created the first children's diabetic clinic and first joint diabetes-pregnancy clinic; *p85-86*.

MAURICE LESSOF (b 1924)
Professor of Medicine at Guy's and later UMDS (1971-1989); authority on allergy; *p83*.

JOHN CHARLES LEVER (1811-1859)
Guy's physician; first to describe presence of protein in the urine of pregnant women with eclampsia; *p53*.

SIR AUBREY LEWIS (1900-1975)
Psychiatrist; first director of the Institute of Psychiatry; key role in making psychiatry an academic discipline; established the MRC Social Psychiatry Research Unit; *p59-60*.

LORD LISTER (JOSEPH LISTER) OM FRS (1827-1912)
Pioneer of antisepsis in surgery; appointed Professor of Surgery at King's College London (1877); dramatically reduced mortality rates for major operations; President, Royal Society 1895-1900; *p11, 69*.

ROBERT McCANCE FRS (1898-1993)
Clinical scientist and head of King's College Hospital biochemistry laboratory; with Elsie Widdowson wrote nutritionist bible, *The Chemical Composition of Foods*; studied the effects of nutrition; *p45*.

RONALD MACKEITH (1908-1977)
Paediatrician; key role in introducing developmental child neurology in UK; initiated the Paediatric Research Unit, Guy's (1960); founded the Mac Keith Press and the journal *Developmental Medicine and Child Neurology*; *p57*.

FREDERIC HENRY HORATIO AKBAR MAHOMED (1849-1884)
Alumnus and physician, Guy's; organized system for the registration of diseases for the British Association; produced sphygmographic evidence of arterio-capillary fibrosis; wrote on the early stages of scarlatinal nephritis; *p91, 92*.

MICHAEL MAISEY (b 1939)
Guy's alumnus; Philip Harris Chair of Radiological Sciences 1984-2002; development of isotope scanning, PET, image-guided interventions; configuration of MRI, X-ray and ultrasound; *p42*.

(CHARLES) DAVID MARSDEN FRS (1938-1998)
St Thomas' alumnus; Professor and Head of the Department of Neurology at the IoP (1972-1987); defined dystonias as neurological, not psychiatric, disorders; described neurological effects of neuroleptic drugs; *p37*.

HENRY MAUDSLEY (1835-1918)
Medical psychologist; in 1907, contributed £30,000 for a hospital for early treatment of mental illness and for psychiatric research, resulting in the Maudsley Hospital (opened in 1923) and an annual lecture in his name; *p10, 59-60*.

RICHARD MEAD FRS (1673-1754)
Physician, St Thomas'; devised a method of tapping for dropsy which greatly reduced the incidence of syncope; wrote government advice on plague and smallpox; helped to establish the practice of inoculation; *p8, 67-69*.

ANTHONY D MILNER (b 1938)
Professor of Neonatology, St Thomas' Hospital; ensured that neonatal ventilation is based on sound physiological principles and scientific evidence; *p84*.

JOHN LAWS MILTON (1820-1898)
Founder of St John's Hospital for Diseases of the Skin; studied skin disease and venereal disease; first description of angioneurotic oedema (also known as Milton's urticaria or Quincke's oedema); *p89*.

ALEXANDER MOWAT (1935-1995)
First Professor of Paediatric Hepatology in UK; developed paediatric hepatology and transplantation at King's College Hospital; *p58, 94*.

FLORENCE NIGHTINGALE OM (1820-1910)
Reformer of nursing, army medicine and hospital organisation; pioneer in use of medical statistics; established the Nightingale School of Nursing; first woman to receive the Order of Merit (1907); *p9, 70, 105-106*.

HUMPHREY OSMOND (1917-2004)
Psychiatrist; alumnus, Guy's; identified adrenochrome as a cause of schizophrenia and pioneered use of vitamin B3 to counter it; used hallucinogenic drugs in treatment of alcoholism; coined term 'psychedelic'; fundamental contributions to environmental psychology.

VICTOR PARSONS (1929-1995)
Nephrologist; founded renal unit at King's College Hospital; improved methods of dialysis and kidney transplantation for diabetic patients; *p86, 91, 92.*

FREDERICK WILLIAM PAVY FRS (1829-1911)
Alumnus, physician and physiologist, Guy's; described intermittent proteinuria; *p86-87.*

PAUL POLANI FRS (1914-2006)
Professor of Paediatric Research and first Director of the Paediatric Research Unit, Guy's (1960); analysis of chromosomal defects affecting XY chromosomes; the Polani Research Library was founded in 1963; *p28.*

URBAN PRITCHARD (1845-1925)
First Professor of Aural Surgery in UK at King's (1866); research into anatomy and function of the inner ear.

FRANCIS T G PRUNTY (1910-1979)
Endocrinologist; Professor of Clinical Pathology, St Thomas' Hospital Medical School; founder of the International Society of Endocrinology; showed beneficial effects of corticosteroids on asthma; *p81.*

DAVID PYKE CBE (1921-2001)
Consultant Physician and Head of the Diabetic Department at King's College Hospital; Registrar of the Royal College of Physicians (1975-1992); research on twins produced important insights into causes and complications of diabetes; *p87.*

SIR JOHN RANDALL FRS (1905-1984)
Wheatstone Chair of Physics at King's College London (1946) and founding director of MRC Biophysics Research Unit, where Wilkins and Franklin studied DNA and Hanson muscle; *p21-22, 25-26.*

GEORGE OWEN REES FRS (1813-1889)
Physician, lecturer and alumnus, Guy's; studied albuminuria (1833); chemistry of urine; proposed new method of measuring sugar in diabetic blood; *p86-87.*

SIR HAROLD LLOYD NICHOLAS RIDLEY FRS (1906-2001)
Alumnus, St Thomas'; appointed ophthalmic surgeon, St Thomas' (1947); pioneered intraocular lens transplantation (1951), an operation since performed on around 200 million people worldwide; *p10, 101-104.*

GERARD RUSSELL (b 1928)
Established the Eating Disorder Unit in 1979 at the Institute of Psychiatry; gave the first modern description of bulimia nervosa categorising it as 'an ominous variant of anorexia nervosa'; *p48.*

SIR MICHAEL RUTTER CBE FRS (b 1933)
Psychiatrist; alumnus Maudsley; founder and Director of the MRC Child Psychiatry Unit at the IoP; founder and Director of the MRC Social, Genetic and Developmental Psychiatry Centre; established child psychiatry as an academic discipline; *p61.*

DAME CICELY SAUNDERS OM (1918-2005)
Founder of the first modern hospice and initiator of a worldwide hospice and palliative care movement; alumna of St Thomas', training as a nurse, lady almoner and doctor; *p77-80.*

EDWARD PETER SHARPEY-SCHAFER (1908-1963)
Professor of Medicine, St Thomas'; studied peripheral circulation; *p96.*

JON SCOPES (1920-1999)
Paediatrician; developed neonatal intensive care St Thomas' Hospital; *p58.*

SIR CHARLES SCOTT SHERRINGTON FRS (1857-1952)
Physiologist; alumnus, St Thomas'; coined the term 'synapse'; two major theories – 'the final common pathway' and 'the integrative action of the nervous system' – provided the foundation for modern understanding of the nervous system; awarded 1932 Nobel prize in Physiology or Medicine (with E D Adrian); President of the Royal Society 1920-1925; *p37.*

ROBERT SIMMONS FRS (b 1938)
Professor of Biophysics, King's College London; contributed significantly to the understanding of muscle contraction; *p22, 24.*

SIR JOHN SIMON FRS (1816-1904)
Demonstrator in anatomy, King's College London; lecturer in anatomical pathology, surgeon and alumnus, St Thomas' Hospital; First Medical Officer of Health to City of London; sanitation reformer; *p49-50, 70.*

ELIOT SLATER (1904-1983)
Psychiatrist; founder and Director of the Psychiatric Genetics Unit at the Institute of Psychiatry (1959); established the Maudsley Hospital Twin Register, enabling future psychiatric genetic studies; *p61.*

AUDREY SMITH (1915-1981)
Physiologist, main founder of cryobiology; alumna King's College London and clinical pathologist at King's (1943-1944).

PETER SONKSEN (b 1936)
Professor of Endocrinology, St Thomas'; studied effect of stepped insulin doses, leading to low-dose insulin infusion as a treatment for diabetic ketoacidosis; *p86.*

EDGAR SOWTON (1930-1994)
Director of Cardiac Services at Guy's Hospital in 1970; involved in the development of cardiac pacemakers and also one of the first people in the UK to carry out cardiac angioplasty; *p98.*

ERNEST H STARLING FRS (1866-1927)
Physiologist; described formation of oedema; Starling's law, describing a fundamental property of cardiac muscle; *p91, 95-96, 99.*

SIR GEORGE FREDERIC STILL (1868-1941)
Paediatrician; alumnus, Guy's; Physician for Diseases of Children at King's College Hospital (1899); first Professor of the Diseases of Children in the UK (at King's College London, 1906); first president of British Paediatric Association; identified the chronic rheumatoid arthritis peculiar to children now called Still's Disease; *p55, 56-57.*

ALEC STOKES (1919-2003)
Mathematical physicist; contributed to interpreting the structure of DNA; *p26, 30.*

SIR ERIC STROUD (1924-2005)
Paediatrician; key role in the creation of Variety Club Children's Hospital at King's College Hospital; set up first clinics for children with sickle cell anaemia; *p58.*

JOHN LOUIS WILLIAM THUDICHUM (1829-1901)
Physician and chemist; chemical research into disease under John Simon; lecturer and first director of a new laboratory of chemistry and pathology at St Thomas' Hospital medical school (1865-1871); pioneer in applying spectrum analysis to biological materials; discovered 'luteines' (carotenoids) 1869; published studies on the chemistry of the brain (1874); *p36.*

SIR NESTOR TIRARD (1853-1928)
Physician, King's College Hospital, Professor of *Materia Medica* and Pharmacology (1885-1900); Professor of the Principles and Practice of Medicine (1900-1919); one of the earliest experts on renal disease in childhood; *p91.*

ROBERT BENTLEY TODD FRS (1809-1860)
Physician and physiologist; reformed medical education at King's College London and later reformed nursing; established the first scholarships for medical students in England; key role in establishing King's College Hospital; identified Todd's paralysis, afferent and efferent nerves, astereognosis, and hypertrophic cirrhosis of the liver; *p9, 10, 15, 35.*

MICHAEL TYNAN (b 1934)
Professor of Paediatric Cardiology, UMDS; innovator of non-surgical procedures to treat congenital heart disease; *p99.*

HUGH DE WARDENER CBE (b 1916)
Nephrologist; alumnus and lecturer, St Thomas'; worked on renal physiology, salt and water balance and acute renal failure; *The Kidney* (1958); *p93.*

PETER WATKINS (b 1935)
Consultant Diabetologist; worked with Victor Parsons on the dialysis and kidney transplantion of diabetes patients; *p86.*

WILLIAM CHARLES WELLS (1757-1817)
American-born physician, St Thomas' Hospital; research on scarlet fever and dropsy; proposed that protein in urine originated in blood; theories of inheritance and selection, foreshadowing Darwin; *p91.*

THOMAS WHARTON (1614-1673)
Physician at St Thomas'; published first account of the glands in *Adenographia*; named the thyroid gland, Wharton's duct and Wharton's jelly; directed careful dissection towards a physiological understanding of human anatomical structures; *p7, 13-14.*

RICHARD WHITE (b 1930)
Nephrologist; set up children's renal unit at Guy's; *p91.*

ELSIE WIDDOWSON CBE FRS (1906-2000)
Nutritionist; alumna, King's College London; with Robert McCance wrote nutritionist bible, *The Chemical Composition of Foods*; studied the effects of nutrition; *p45.*

MAURICE WILKINS CBE FRS (1916-2004)
Professor of Biophysics at King's; awarded Nobel Prize for Physiology or Medicine for discovery of the structure of DNA (1962); *p10, 21, 22, 25-27, 30.*

SIR SAMUEL WILKS FRS (1824-1911)
Alumnus, Guy's; one of the editors of Guy's Hospital Reports; observations on tertiary syphilis; showed the importance of post-mortem examinations for clinical practice; *p19, 69, 73.*

CICELY DELPHINE WILLIAMS (1893-1992)
Paediatrician and nutritionist; alumna of King's Medical School; identified kwashiorkor; in 1948 appointed first head of the maternal and child health section of the WHO; adviser to Family Planning Association; *p57.*

ROGER WILLIAMS CBE (b 1931)
King's College Hospital and Medical School (1966-1996); Professor of Hepatology and Consultant Physician and Director of the Institute of Liver Studies; established Liver Unit (1966); collaboration with Professor Sir Roy Calne to perform first liver transplants in UK (1968); *p93.*

HERBERT WILSON (b 1929)
Physicist, King's College London; expert in X-ray diffraction; *p27, 30.*

KINNIER WILSON (1874-1937)
First head in the UK of a medical school department of neurology; description of eponymous disease; *p36.*

ANTHONY WING (b 1933)
Nephrologist at St Thomas'; development of the European Registry of Dialysis and Transplantation; *p91-92.*

MAUREEN YOUNG (b 1915)
One of the first women to join the Physiology Department at St Thomas' Hospital Medical School after the war; one of the founder members of the Neonatal Society (President 1984-1987); developed methods of measuring oxygen in the newborn's blood and new ventilators; *p84.*

JOHN YUDKIN (1910-1995)
First UK and King's Professor of Nutrition 1954-1971; wrote books on the subject of slimming with a scientific basis; pointed to sugar as a cause of coronary heart disease; *p45-46, 47.*

Acknowledgments

We thank David Bradley, Caroline Cross, Adrian Hayday and Christine Kenyon Jones for their contributions to the following chapters:
The cell: dissecting the new anatomy (Caroline Cross);
A fundamental discovery in immunology: Peter Gorer and murine H-2 (David Bradley and Adrian Hayday);
The mind & body interface: developments in neuroscience (David Bradley);
We are what we eat: the science of nutrition (Christine Kenyon Jones);
Growth of paediatrics & child health (Christine Kenyon Jones);
Health in mind: psychiatry & psychiatric research (Christine Kenyon Jones);
From test-tube to treatment: pharmaceutical sciences (Caroline Cross);
Making inroads: cancer studies & research (Caroline Cross);
At the end of life: Dame Cicely Saunders & palliative care (Christine Kenyon-Jones);
The heart of the matter: cardiovascular medicine and science (Caroline Cross);
War & medicine (Christine Kenyon Jones);
Medicine & the arts (Christine Kenyon Jones).

We thank the following and their organisations for their help with this book:

June Almeida; Stephanie Amiel; Jonathan Barker; Averil Baxter; Jennifer Best; Christopher Buckland-Wright; Kevin Burnand; Peter Burney; Stewart Cameron; Sir Cyril Chantler; Margaret Delaney; Andrew Dyer; Bill Edwards; Mathias Gautel; Anne Greenough; Adrian Hayday; Robert Hider; Brandon High; Walter Holland; Simon Howell; Richard Hughes; Brian Hurwitz; Roger Jones; David Langdon; Tak Lee; Harry Keen; Michael Malim; Chris Mathew; Ian McFarlane; Mike Messer; Stephen Minger; John Moxham; Michael O'Brien; Tony Ng; Lucilla Poston; Edward Reynolds; The Royal Society; Robin Saklatvala; Katie Sambrook; Hugh Saxton; David Scott; Ajay Shah; John Sleep; Ellen Solomon; Susan Standring; Jennifer Strid; Antonella Surdi; George Szmukler; Hywel Thomas; Ian Thompson; Janet Treasure; Peter Watkins; Bert Williams, Black History Brighton and Hove Black History; Roger Williams; Steven Williams.

We would particularly like to thank:

King's College London, Archives and Corporate Records Services for the reproduction of the following images: John Randall (p21, 22, 25); Eric Stroud (p55); Nestor Tirard (p89).

King's College London, Foyle Special Collections Library for the reproduction of the following images: Cover of William Chesleden's The Anatomy of the Human Body (p14); cover of William Cheselden's Osteographia (p14) and illustrations from Astley Cooper's Anatomy of the Breast (p15).

All images contained in this book are owned by King's College London, with the exception of the following:

Bethlem Hospital (p7), King Edward VI (p7); Anatomical dissection c1524 (p7); William Cheselden dissection scene (p12); Haighton's forceps (p53); John Haighton (p53); Richard Mead extract (p68); The Great Plague in London (p68); John Simon cartoon (p49) © Wellcome Library, London.

Sickle cell image (p30) © EM Unit/Royal Free Medical School/Wellcome Photo Library; MRSA image (p72) © Wellcome Photo Library; Woman eating cake (p88) © Anthea Sieveking/Wellcome Photo Library; E. coli image (p93) © David Gregory and Debbie Marshall/ Wellcome Photo Library.

Cicely Saunders (cover, p80); GDH Cole (p86); William Briggs (p104); John Keats (p109); Somerset Maugham (p109); John Keats (p110) © National Portrait Gallery.

Dissecting room at Guy's (p16) © Karen Ingham.

Thomas Wharton (cover, p7, 13) © The Royal College of Physicians of London.

Gray's Anatomy (p16) reproduced by kind permission of Elsevier Publishing, UK.

Peter Baker (p35); Robert McCance (p45); Richard Doll (p74); Ronald Thomson Grant (p95, 105) © The Godfrey Argent Studio.

James Danielli (p21). Every effort was made to contact the copyright holder of this image.

Robert Simmons (p21); John Louis William Thudichum (p35); David Ferrier (p35); Frederick Gowland Hopkins (p46); John Simon (p49, 67); George Owen Rees (p85) © The Royal Society.

Rosalind Franklin (cover, p25) reproduced by kind permission of the Novartis Foundation.

George Snell (p32); Marijuana leaf (p61); Mature and young hands (p79); © Getty Images.

David Marsden *(p35)* by David Graham reproduced by kind permission of UCL Institute of Neurology.

Arnold Bender *(p45)* reproduced by kind permission of David Bender.

Elsie Widdowson *(p45)* reproduced by kind permission of the MRC Centre, Cambridge.

'Death's dispensary' *(p49)* © Mary Evans Picture Library

'A royal visit to the Evelina Hospital' *(p56)* © Illustrated London News Picture Library, London.

'Sun bounces off the new Evelina Children's Hospital' *(p56)* by Dan Dunkley; 'Patients, local children and staff celebrate at the opening of the new Evelina Children's Hospital' *(p56)* and 'Children enjoy the Evelina Children's Hospital's 17-foot high helter skelter' *(p56)*, by Robert Aberman; reproduced by kind permission of Guy's and St Thomas' NHS Foundation Trust.

Cicely Williams *(p57)*. Every effort was made to contact the copyright holder of this image.

Down's Syndrome boy *(p62)* reproduced by kind permission of Down's Syndrome Association, UK.

Arnold Beckett *(p63)* © Topfoto.

Hepcidin – an iron regulatory hormone (p65) reproduced by kind permission of Peter Crowther.

Frederick Heaf *(p70)* reproduced by kind permission of Special Collections and Archives, University of Cardiff.

Dame Cicely Saunders *(p77)* by Mary McCartney Donald reproduced by kind permission of the Cicely Saunders Foundation.

Richard Cope painting of Thomas Guy, Richard Mead and architect *(p78)* reproduced by kind permission of Guy's and St

Thomas' Charity.

Asthmatic boy *(p83)* reproduced by kind permission of the National Asthma Campaign.

H G Wells *(p86)* reproduced by kind permission of Diabetes UK.

Mahomed sphygmograph *(p92)* by Donald Blaufox reproduced by kind permission of the United States National Library of Medicine.

Hugh de Wardener *(p93)* by Neville Miles reproduced by kind permission of Imperial College London.

Norman Browse *(p95)*; William Kelsey Fry *(p105)*; facial surgery paintings by artist Henry Tonks *(p106)*; reproduced by kind permission of the President and Council of the Royal College of Surgeons of England.

Mouse Cleaver's Hurricane *(p102)* by John Howard Worsley, reproduced by kind permission of the artist.

Harold Ridley *(p103)* © EMPICS.

Florence Nightingale *(cover; p9, 67, 105)*; Florence Nightingale in the Military Hospital at Scutari *(p106)*; Battle of Inkerman *(p106)*; courtesy of the Florence Nightingale Museum Trust, London.

Ludwig Wittgenstein *(p107)* reproduced by kind permission of the Wittgenstein Archive, Cambridge.

Troops in Iraq 2004 *(p108)* courtesy of the US Army.

Bust of Joseph Henry Green *(p109)*; Weekes, Henry (1807-1877) Royal Academy London, England, 1863, marble h. 31 inches © Conway Library, Courtauld Institute of Art, London.

Andrew Motion *(p110)* © Antonio Zaueta Olmos.

Scene from 'Tales of Hoffman' *(p111)* © Clive Barda and Arena PAL images.

Frozen hand *(p112)* © Deborah Padfield.

Body imaging (cover) © Mehau Kulyk/Science Photo Library;
Cell membrane sugars *(p24)* © Hybrid Medical Animation/ Science Photo Library;
Breast cancer mammogram *(p29)* © Zephyr/Science Photo Library;
Sectioned brains: Alzheimer's disease vs normal *(p39)* © Alfred. Paseika/Science Photo Library;
Anorexia nervosa: girl examines figure at mirror *(p48)* © Oscar Burriel/Science Photo Library;
Four month foetus *(p58)* © Edelmann/Science Photo Library;
Heaf test *(p70)* © Biophoto Associates/Science Photo Library;
Malarial blood cells *(p72)* © D Ferguson/Science Photo Library;
Sun Protection *(p76)* © Mauro Fermariello/Science Photo Library;
Premature baby *(p84)* © Tina Stallard/Science Photo Library;
The diabetic foot ulcer *(p87)* © BSIP, James Cavallini/Science Photo Library;
Heart pacemaker *(p98)* © PHT/Science Photo Library.

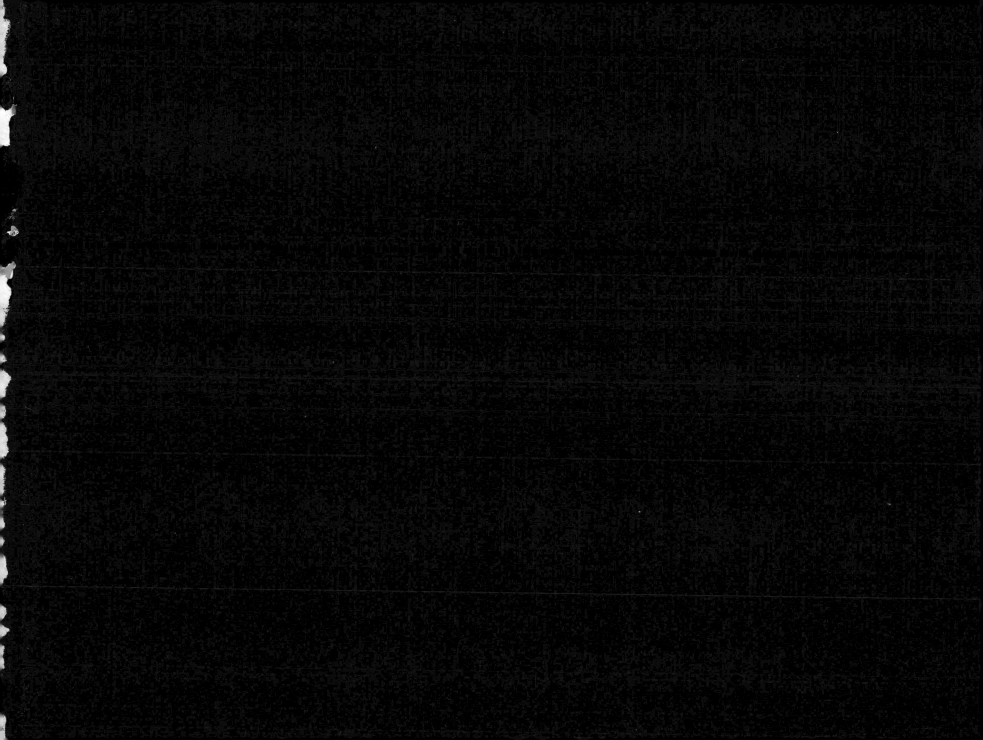